BIRD LOVER'S
WORDSEARCH

Themed puzzles featuring birds from around the world

This edition published in 2023 by Arcturus Publishing Limited
26/27 Bickels Yard, 151–153 Bermondsey Street,
London SE1 3HA

AD010234NT

Printed in the UK

Contents

INTRODUCTION

"In order to see birds it is necessary to become a part of the silence." *Robert Wilson Lynd*

Birds are a source of endless fascination to many from the casual garden observer to the ardent ornithologist. Whether big, bold birds of prey, quirky and unusual birds, or delicate songbirds, they have proven an endless source of inspiration for poetry, art, and music alike.

The puzzles within these pages are all inspired by our fascinating feathered friends—from profiles on individual birds, both common and exotic, to puzzles on birdwatching hotspots, and famous ornithologists. Some of the puzzle grids are accompanied by a word list which has certain words underlined. In these puzzles, the underlined words are the only ones that you need to find within the grid. Where no words are underlined, your task is to find them all!

So, get ready to embark on a grand birdwatching adventure without ever leaving the comfort of home. What will you find when you turn the page?

National Birds

```
E N A R C E U L B L K D V T K
Z D R I B R O T C O D E N A R
E T I K D E R K R K M S O H O
L W O E L T T I L U B I G C T
E O P O O H B W P A B B O M S
Q V U E N U F I R A T I R L E
M U T E S W A N L C G T T A T
K S R T G O S D N O X N N P I
R Y A D N W E I L Y C A A F H
A R G Q A A Z D W H N I B B W
D W S L G T C N M X N G U A P
S Y L L A R M C O C R I C O B
A O E O E H A R P Y E A G L E
W S H S A N O C L A F R Y G U
A U T S A K E R F A L C O N T
```

◊ BALD EAGLE

◊ BARN SWALLOW

◊ BLUE CRANE

◊ COCRICO

◊ CUBAN TROGON

◊ DOCTOR BIRD

◊ EMU

◊ GIANT IBIS

◊ GOLDCREST

◊ GYRFALCON

◊ HARPY EAGLE

◊ HOATZIN

◊ HOOPOE

◊ KIWI

◊ KORI BUSTARD

◊ LITTLE OWL

◊ MUTE SWAN

◊ PALMCHAT

◊ RED KITE

◊ SAKER FALCON

◊ WHITE STORK

```
A I P A R T S A N R L F A D R
D X P W F T A E E I Q R R E N
R D O H R J Z T E L Z I J X K
A R T D G B A D L X B T N C E
T I O S F E Y I R E I Y A S K
S B O T E R B D T I W W U O E
U A O E T E E A R O B O I C H
B L B P O N G L S I R E F K F
T L V H A I A S E G B A R P L
A E S K R K A R E V E L P Y M
E R E F N R A G O N O B I K L
R B Y H U G A K N M V H J O N
G M W C A S S O W A R Y S R R
D U L I Z L L I B N R O H M V
T R A G O P A N R E T A C N I
```

◊ ASTRAPIA

◊ BEE-EATER

◊ CASSOWARY

◊ CORMORANT

◊ CURASSOW

◊ FRIGATEBIRD

◊ GREAT
  BUSTARD

◊ HOATZIN

◊ HORNBILL

◊ IBON

◊ INCA TERN

◊ KAGU

◊ KAKAPO

◊ KEA

◊ KIWI

◊ LYREBIRD

◊ OILBIRD

◊ PAROTIA

◊ POTOO

◊ SAGE-
  GROUSE

◊ SHOEBILL

◊ SHOVELER

◊ TRAGOPAN

◊ UMBRELLA-
  BIRD

Nest-building Sensations

```
G T D C I S T I C O L A S P U
P D R I B R E W O B N Y N W S
G Y R F A L C O N R T C T N L
Y R X Z B A L D E A G L E P W
E B E R G E L T T I L H A O O
T R P T O V E N B I R D L K F
A Z M E A T Z U F O X L O R E
I N A A I E S L O S A O D E E
L J A H Y H E M L W T V N M L
O Q W C T A E E S I W D E A L
R F F I A L B N B F B C P H A
B Q T X P J R Q H T P N O I M
I I P R U A Q B A L G W R M Y
R I U F B R E K C E P D O O W
D P B L A C K K I T E G T M H
```

◊ BALD EAGLE

◊ BARN SWALLOW

◊ BAYA

◊ BEE-EATER

◊ BLACK KITE

◊ BOWERBIRD

◊ BUSHTIT

◊ CISTICOLAS

◊ GYRFALCON

◊ HAMERKOP

◊ HORNBILL

◊ JACANA

◊ LITTLE GREBE

◊ MALLEEFOWL

◊ OROPENDOLA

◊ OVENBIRD

◊ PURPLE MOORHEN

◊ SWIFTLET

◊ TAILORBIRD

◊ WHITE TERN

◊ WOOD-PECKER

A Rainbow of Birds

```
H M A Y S C S S N L G G W Q K
W M L N G O A X O O J R V K R
T H O W Q P T W S S D N E N M
L W I A V P D W M A Y C I E U
Y J I T Y E K V I N F E T S N
W B A N E R B Z R L R G Z S O
H U K A I S P T C V U N L E I
F E R R U G I N O U S A I R L
N Z W O L L E Y F H T R L U L
W J F E O T K S C Y Y O A Z I
O U T V P C N A Y Y U K C A M
R U T I A B E D W O B N I A R
B R N L N P D W A A X H E L E
Y K B O X U Z N M D G M W T V
P Y B U R J R E V L I S K U D
```

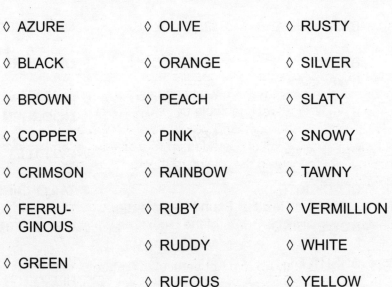

◊ AZURE

◊ BLACK

◊ BROWN

◊ COPPER

◊ CRIMSON

◊ FERRU-
  GINOUS

◊ GREEN

◊ LILAC

◊ OLIVE

◊ ORANGE

◊ PEACH

◊ PINK

◊ RAINBOW

◊ RUBY

◊ RUDDY

◊ RUFOUS

◊ RUSTY

◊ SILVER

◊ SLATY

◊ SNOWY

◊ TAWNY

◊ VERMILLION

◊ WHITE

◊ YELLOW

Bird Profile:
Atlantic Puffin

```
E C A F R U S Y L N I A G N U
B E L O V E D I T P M E T T A
D N A L E C I T A U Q S Y H W
F C O O L E R R S E A B I R D
O L H D I S T I N C T I V E A
R W Y E E S Y E L L O W B C W
A A N I E M C L O W N I R I S
N T J A N K A G S V L O N Y R
G E L I E G S N C L S G N W E
E R N A L C I A K S S A X I M
H T R O N F O I T C M M W N M
V G B W F T X R B R I G H T I
Z A O U V L I T T L E N I E W
L R P H G R A C E F U L T R S
C S E L I N E V U J H D E H S
```

Latin Name: *Fratercula arctica*

Family: *Alcidae*

Description: This squat little seabird has a black crown and back, white undersides, and off-white cheeks. It has bright orange legs and feet but is most recognizable by its bill—a wide triangle that is reddish-orange, charcoal, and yellow—though the brighter parts are shed before winter. All of this adds up to a distinctive and comical-looking bird nicknamed the "clown of the sea". Juveniles are sweetly called pufflings.

Distribution and Habitat: Found in cooler parts of the north Atlantic, with more than 60% of the global population to be found in Iceland.

Fun Fact: Bad at flying and not particularly graceful in flight, puffins make up for this by being excellent swimmers, using their wings to "fly" through the water. When they do attempt flight, they make an ungainly take off, running across the surface of the ocean. It is easy to see why these little birds are beloved by many.

A Mythological Menagerie

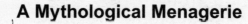

```
N I F F I R G F A S A I P X N
I C C V F I O N N U A L A I U
T S S H Z N S J W H L H Z N Y
S M U P A D A A J N O H T E A
U J R I S M Q S L L H L L O M
M D O A R Z R C A I C A A H A
A P H L I D G O S B C B X P G
D A T Q T N A N S T S A B Z N
E L G U M D B L A H R B N W Q
N K O U R F F I A U T I C T B
A O O S U U B C R C H L X V O
T N H S D N L H A D O G Q T U
E O Z H E N N I A O T P N J H
C S K U U V M E K D H I I E H
Z T X I U Q A C B U C U V Q F
```

◊ ABABIL

◊ AETHON

◊ ALICANTO

◊ ALKONOST

◊ BASAN

◊ BENNU

◊ CALADRIUS

◊ CETAN

◊ CHAMROSH

◊ CHOL

◊ FENGHUANG

◊ FIONNUALA

◊ GAMAYUN

◊ GRIFFIN

◊ HORUS

◊ ITSUMADE

◊ PHOENIX

◊ PIASA

◊ RAIN BIRD

◊ STRIX

◊ THOTH

◊ TURUL

◊ VUCUB
  CAQUIX

◊ ZHENNIAO

Great…

```
D R A T S U B E B E R G D N Z
O M O A U K P I V K L P A G T
O N C O R M O R A N T C E S F
K O S L R R B A F E I S E W I
C C P L A A T N C L E U N A W
U A O I R T Y T E E V E K C S
C R N B O S O P K F G C K A Y
D U E N K R E I O R S T C M K
R T X R U T S T E T E P I N S
A E O O I K T T K S O Y H E U
Z U R H A L V A F M J O T E D
I L W D A X R A M A C A J R P
L B E I A I N E A L E C Q G L
Q E F G N I W E R I H P P A S
T A H B B L A C K H A W K T I
```

◊ ANTPITTA

◊ AUK

◊ BARBET

◊ BLACK-HAWK

◊ BLUE TURACO

◊ BUSTARD

◊ CORMORANT

◊ DUSKY SWIFT

◊ EGRET

◊ ELAENIA

◊ GREBE

◊ GREEN
   MACAW

◊ HORNBILL

◊ IORA

◊ JACAMAR

◊ KISKADEE

◊ KNOT

◊ LIZARD-
   CUCKOO

◊ POTOO

◊ SAPPHIRE-
   WING

◊ SNIPE

◊ THICK-KNEE

◊ WHITE
   PELICAN

◊ XENOPS

To the Nightingale by John Milton

```
P T F O S U O I T I P O R P E
O L I N K E D S S E C C U S D
R A S O O K C U C Y A R P S U
T Y W Y M O O L B F E I L E R
E D L H E L A G N I T H G I N
N R L L E T E R O F D R I B E
D A I L E T I O E Y R R A V S
S E F Y E R H V S A L E E I U
S H A Q M A T E E D S E S E N
E M A M T U D T R Y I O M H G
L J C L O S E A V L E U N I F
E O W H L R D H E L M A Q Q T
P V T A D O O A P O W E R I T
O E S D O O W U H J S T I L L
H S R E V O L T S E L B R A W
```

O nightingale that on yon bloomy spray
Warblest at eve, when all the woods are still,
Thou with fresh hope the lover's heart dost fill,
While the jolly hours lead on propitious May.
Thy liquid notes that close the eye of day,

First heard before the shallow cuckoo's bill,
Portend success in love. O, if Jove's will
Have linked that amorous power to thy soft lay,
Now timely sing, ere the rude bird of hate
Foretell my hopeless doom, in some grove nigh;
As thou from year to year hast sung too late
For my relief, yet hadst no reason why.
Whether the Muse or Love call thee his mate,
Both them I serve, and of their train am I.

Nocturnal Birds

```
G L M E L A G N I T H G I N T
N O O S B S C R E E C H O W L
I O C E A N O R E H T H G I N
U T K E R S P O T T E D O W L
G O I B R F O X J M R K L E H
N P N A E J P K A R M W W Q T
E P G R D I A I I E V A O O U
P O B N O R K A E W X H L E O
E O I O W K A I R P I T A U M
L R R W L K K J A O N H E Q G
T W D L K B E T T S L G R A O
T I E L F O W L P H O I O R R
I L W O O D C O C K G N B U F
L L T O R R A P T H G I N A P
E K A R C N R O C T Y R N P K
```

◊ BARN OWL

◊ BARRED OWL

◊ BOREAL OWL

◊ CORNCRAKE

◊ ELF OWL

◊ FROGMOUTH

◊ KAKAPO

◊ KIWI

◊ LITTLE PENGUIN

◊ MOCKING-BIRD

◊ NIGHT HAWK

◊ NIGHT HERON

◊ NIGHT PARROT

◊ NIGHTINGALE

◊ NIGHTJAR

◊ PAURAQUE

◊ POORWILL

◊ POTOO

◊ SCREECH-OWL

◊ SPOTTED OWL

◊ WOODCOCK

Birds with Seven-letter Names – Part One

```
H N H A D G N I W P A L P G Y
C D I L K C E N Y R W T I A L
I R E L B R A W I G U H N E A
R A M E T L L A W D A G T M Z
T M H S H A F N L P D M A O T
S A P O Y A V A E U V N I O E
O C E R S D R A L L A M L R U
E A A H R E C R M K W G P H Q
U J F R M O W D I E R R I E G
Q S O E C A C N E E I J K N N
I Q W K G E W B Y Y R R N R I
C E L C A O I L V V O T E T W
A M A I Q L A C W U V S N S X
C Y W L L G E X P S W G U H A
C J J F W L L I B X A W E W W
```

◊ CACIQUE   ◊ MALLARD   ◊ QUETZAL

◊ EMERALD   ◊ MANAKIN   ◊ ROSELLA

◊ FLICKER   ◊ MOORHEN   ◊ SERIEMA

◊ GADWALL   ◊ NILTAVA   ◊ WARBLER

◊ GREYLAG   ◊ OSTRICH   ◊ WAXBILL

◊ HARRIER   ◊ PEACOCK   ◊ WAXWING

◊ JACAMAR   ◊ PEAFOWL   ◊ WEEBILL

◊ LAPWING   ◊ PINTAIL   ◊ WRYNECK

Bird Profile: Blue Jay

```
M S E N I L E R O H S R U A F
A T K S Y A L P S I D E Y O S
R S G N I K C I M I M G U K K
K E M S O A W A Q E T N W E I
I R I C T W L U L T D A A P L
N O M A H N N A U L H D R P L
G F I T E A N F R Y S E L D T
S Y C T R I T S S M S U R S S
O E R E N Y T K I E M I A O R
N A Y R R A S E N A H E O U E
G S A S T N I C G B R O W N H
B I J E A G E E S B Y O T D T
I L S M C A N A D A L E E S A
R Y U M I G R A T I N G R A E
D H R E F L E C T S H A R P F
```

Latin Name: *Cyanocitta cristata*

Family: *Corvidae*

Description: The blue jay is a large member of the songbird family and is most easily recognized by its lavender-blue plumage. It has a tufty crest on its head, a pale breast, and black and white markings.

A noisy bird, the blue jay makes its presence known when it sounds the alarm at signs of danger such as mimicking hawks to alert others to the presence of the bird of prey.

Sounds: The blue jay sings, makes sharp alarm calls, and has some skill in the mimicry of both humans and other birds.

Distribution and Habitat: They are found in forests and migrating flocks around shorelines in the United States and parts of Canada.

Fun Fact: The feathers are not actually blue, the pigmentation is melanin, which is brown, but it reflects and scatters light in such a way that it displays the distinctive blue the bird is known for.

```
R E V O L P D E G N I R P B H
R O O T A K C O C Y F U N U C
N O E G I P N E E R G R I T N
K B C W O O D S T A R D G T I
W R E K C E P D O O W G H O F
A W A T T L E B I R D R T N A
H H I Q G H G B R U E Q J Q C
W I P K D B R E Q H L O A U N
O T P K N D E U S E G G R A I
R E W E Y K T I S O A V U I Z
R T I O N V F Z Q H E K L L I
A E F J R G T I N A M O U Y L
P R H I N C U D N U V U B C Y
S N M I W F R I A R B I R D O
M O K F Q S Y I N W E L R U C
```

◊ BUTTONQUAIL

◊ COCKATOO

◊ CROW

◊ CURLEW

◊ EAGLE

◊ EGRET

◊ FRIARBIRD

◊ GREEN-
PIGEON

◊ GULL

◊ INCA-FINCH

◊ KINGFISHER

◊ NIGHTJAR

◊ PENGUIN

◊ RINGED
PLOVER

◊ ROCK-
THRUSH

◊ SPARROW-
HAWK

◊ SWIFT

◊ TINAMOU

◊ WATTLEBIRD

◊ WHITE-TERN

◊ WOOD-
PECKER

◊ WOODSTAR

Birds Beginning with "T"

```
T E R I A L L I B N R O H T A
T O L I M A D O V E T Y R M L
T K D R I B T N A R Y T E A A
I T E P U I W R E N A U P A I
G T I N K E R B I R D F E T L
E U P U T T T A T O T T E O Y
R R E H S A R H T R N E R M H
S K E L R K T F I A A D C T T
H E R E T A W L C O K J E I I
R Y T T N H L U T L D A E T T
I T V A S E O W T M H Y R W P
K I G U R T R E E M A R T I N
E E R T I T M O U S E F Z T G
R H T I N A M O U H A T E E A
T C H A G R A L A I P U O R T
```

◊ TAKAHE

◊ TANAGER

◊ TCHAGRA

◊ TEPUI WREN

◊ THORNBILL

◊ THRASHER

◊ THRUSH

◊ TIGER SHRIKE

◊ TINAMOU

◊ TINKERBIRD

◊ TIT HYLIA

◊ TITMOUSE

◊ TOLIMA DOVE

◊ TOMTIT

◊ TOUCAN

◊ TREE MARTIN

◊ TREE-
   CREEPER

◊ TREEPIE

◊ TRILLER

◊ TROUPIAL

◊ TUFTED JAY

◊ TURKEY

◊ TWITE

◊ TYRANT BIRD

```
R O C A H C M H S C R E E C H
Y Y H E D E R R A B G D Q Z R
G N W C L R J T Z Z E R B L O
F X S Q O G A C T G D R A W L
O O U A J W A F G Q Q S L S H
J L B A N D B E L L I E D W S
B H D Y I H L D I H T R A K H
P Y G M Y E D K D N S A Y I R
F U P D R E D E K S A M T G W
E J R A T A T I A L A M O O L
A Y B F V P D F D E N R O H I
R H U C C C D Y E C Z D S L T
F T Q A T D E C A F Y H S A T
U S C O P S O R I E N T A L L
L U P G N I W O R R U B I H E
```

◊ ASHY-FACED

◊ BAND-
  BELLIED

◊ BARE-
  LEGGED

◊ BARRED

◊ BURROWING

◊ CHACO

◊ EAGLE

◊ FEARFUL

◊ GRASS

◊ HORNED

◊ LITTLE

◊ MALAITA

◊ MASKED

◊ OMANI

◊ ORIENTAL

◊ OWLET

◊ PYGMY

◊ SCOPS

◊ SCREECH

◊ SERAM

◊ SOOTY

◊ TAWNY

◊ TUFTED

◊ WOOD

A Flock of Ducks

```
R S E S S E L T H G I L F M K
M H H V S O R I N O C O A M C
E E N O M Y X O M S N N Y S A
R L U K E C Y A P S D T T P B
G D S L W I L E H A R E L P S
A U L C B L C A R B A R S B A
N C Z L A T F I Y M Z R C A V
S K I R A U N H E S E A O I N
E L D C L W P R J C A L T K A
R D L V Y P D N V U O N E A C
R E O M V L J A O E D T R L R
D U W I F V O D G E T Y T E V
S F O I X E B Z J S G E D O B
N G O L D E N E Y E Y I A P N
S R D B G A R G A N E Y W L C
```

◊ BAIKAL ◊ GARGANEY ◊ SCOTER

◊ BLUE ◊ GOLDENEYE ◊ SHELDUCK

◊ CANVASBACK ◊ LAYSAN ◊ SMEW

◊ COTTON ◊ MALLARD ◊ SPECTACLED

◊ EIDER ◊ MANDARIN ◊ STEAMER

◊ FLIGHTLESS ◊ MERGANSER ◊ TEAL

◊ FULVOUS ◊ ORINOCO ◊ WIGEON

◊ GADWALL ◊ SCAUP ◊ WOOD

```
T A P A C U L O T A S I T Y B
R U M B R E L L A B I R D A D
D R I B G N I K A D B F I G T
G L N L E A M N Z R I L N N Y
N R Q D T L T E I O E U J I R
A D C G Q S L S V R V N C T A
T Q A T H A T B E E W E P O N
E W J R E L A O I B N P F C N
A B I N E Z L T T R E W B Q U
T K I B Z Q L C T I D O D E L
E A I S P A D E B I L L H V E
R R I F L E M A N K P L R P T
D O A Z A T I J N O M T A B U
F S H A R P B I L L W N N G K
E E D A K S I K N I K A N A M
```

◊ ANTPITTA	◊ GALLITO	◊ PHOEBE
◊ ANTSHRIKE	◊ GNATEATER	◊ RIFLEMAN
◊ ASITY	◊ KINGBIRD	◊ SHARPBILL
◊ BELLBIRD	◊ KISKADEE	◊ SPADEBILL
◊ BRISTLEBIRD	◊ LARK	◊ TAPACULO
◊ COTINGA	◊ MANAKIN	◊ TYRANNULET
◊ DIUCON	◊ MONJITA	◊ UMBRELLA BIRD
◊ ELAENIA	◊ PEWEE	◊ WAGTAIL

Bird Profile: Mourning Dove

```
S P O T T E D R A W I N G M D
W H I S T L I N G P N A O R E
Y L I M A F V A R I O U S E L
S L E N D E R E G D R E E L L
N U S E Y V D N N N T M P A I
S C F T K A I A I S H O M P K
C E L F T O L N R W I N R T S
A E H O O D G E A N W O H A E
R N R C O U B T T O T G S I H
I S G O N M S E N E I A T B T
B N W I E A D K C L R M O R A
B I Z M E E R T F A A O P U B
E A F R G F I B T O I U S B A
A L B G D N U O R G N S W U D
N P S T G T D N U O F N E S T
```

Latin Name: *Zenaida macroura*

Family: *Columbidae*

Description: The mourning dove is mostly a plain, light ashy-brown, paler on the breast, and has dark spots on the wing. It is a medium-sized member of the dove family and is slender with a long, pointed tail.

Mourning doves are usually monogamous and so are frequently spotted in pairs. They lie on tree branches and on the ground to bathe in both the sun and rain.

Sounds: Like many members of the dove family, the mourning dove makes a distinctive cooing sound. When taking off and in flight the wings make a light whistling sound.

Distribution and Habitat: The are found in various habitats, from woodland to suburbia, across North America and the Caribbean.

Fun Fact: The mourning dove is a skilled flier which can often out-manoeuvre predators. It is also known to feign injury, drawing predators away from its nest and so protecting its eggs.

```
E R I H P P A S N T H L U H T
H B E C V M Z E F E I A F B E
L L I B E C N A L F L O R A L
N A W R L R E A P Q L E H R T
L I Z L A L A I W O S T H B N
I S B U L C I E L S T T E T O
A N U O L I N B T J A E R H R
T O C N C I B U E E R U M R F
N W F K B A N L J L L Q I O R
R C K M V E J E W M K O T A A
O A T R A M A T N A S C I T T
H P D L A R E M E N X V I V S
T M O U N T A I N G E M N S F
Y E T A N S T E N O R O C R R
T S E R C R E V O L P I A V T
```

◊ AWLBILL

◊ BARBTHROAT

◊ CARIB

◊ COQUETTE

◊ CORONET

◊ EMERALD

◊ HERMIT

◊ HILLSTAR

◊ INCA

◊ JACOBIN

◊ LANCEBILL

◊ LAZULINE

◊ MANGO

◊ MOUNTAIN-
GEM

◊ PLOVER-
CREST

◊ SANTA MARTA

◊ SAPPHIRE

◊ SICKLEBILL

◊ SNOWCAP

◊ STAR-
FRONTLET

◊ SUNBEAM

◊ THORNTAIL

◊ TOPAZ

◊ VIOLETEAR

```
E T C T R U M P E T E R D D L
E N A I C Q C L E S A O P E L
O N I D T R P N X L U F P D O
L N O P D R E V L V M O G O P
E B E S U R I I T S P R H O D
K R N P I Y G L H Z E X H H E
H A W F I N C H C E A C Y P R
C M E N I C W R N L N R R Y K
N B N R E B Y F I I S O A R A
I L F I M M I D F N E S N R E
F I W Q K N E E L N R S A H B
D N V R C S S L L E O B C U S
L G M H E O I S U T Z I C L O
O Z P R R K L S B N A L B A R
G T T N A E P O R U E L M G G
```

◊ AZORES

◊ BRAMBLING

◊ BULLFINCH

◊ CANARY

◊ CITRIL

◊ CROSSBILL

◊ DESERT

◊ EUROPEAN

◊ FRINGILLA

◊ GOLDFINCH

◊ GREENFINCH

◊ GROSBEAK

◊ HAWFINCH

◊ HOODED

◊ HOUSE

◊ LINNET

◊ PINE

◊ PURPLE

◊ PYRRHULA

◊ REDPOLL

◊ ROSEFINCH

◊ SISKIN

◊ TENERIFE

◊ TRUMPETER

```
D J O Z N O E G I W N W R H Y
O X G O L D E N O R I O L E S
T R E H C T A C R E T S Y O D
T E A G L E O W L L R P J F R
E E N Y A J W F F B A A R B I
R N W N I S E H L R M R A U B
E K X A I W L F I A G R J L K
L K P S D L R E G W A O T L C
U C K H G K U Y Q D R W H F A
C I P O S R C T N E C H G I L
N H E B I D I A A E H A I N B
K T Y B U U P F J R C W N C R
L W O Y M G Y P F R X K J H I
H O O P O E F W O O D C O C K
C H I F F C H A F F N J L Z B
```

◇ BLACKBIRD

◇ BULLFINCH

◇ CHIFFCHAFF

◇ CRAG MARTIN

◇ CURLEW

◇ DOTTEREL

◇ EAGLE-OWL

◇ GOLDEN ORIOLE

◇ GRIFFON

◇ HOBBY

◇ HOOPOE

◇ JACKDAW

◇ JAY

◇ LINNET

◇ NIGHTJAR

◇ OYSTER-CATCHER

◇ PYGMY OWL

◇ REED WARBLER

◇ SISKIN

◇ SPARROW-HAWK

◇ THICK-KNEE

◇ WIGEON

◇ WOODCOCK

◇ WRYNECK

Words Which Come Before/After Bird

```
E T O J I R E K G M Z I K B F
L O X Y R Y O N Z W W U C R J
T T B T H Q I E Y H J E A A P
T B H G X M A S E I T L L I D
A U G U M P U N S R B F B N C
W O E U N L V A Y L A I C E Q
P H H M M D N K E Y T R N D D
C R O M S Y E E G H H T N R W
I O O U O N R R S A S E A K A
F F B L S C O K E I S Y W C T
W C R H I E K W F E G U A H C
A J O I B A A I E Y R G R D H
T R P L A R T D N T E A E F I
E H U O Q R I W J G D E E R N
R E Q J G E R T O C F Z F G G
```

◊ BATH	◊ HUMMING	◊ SURF
◊ BLACK	◊ MOCKING	◊ TAILOR
◊ BLUE	◊ REED	◊ THUNDER
◊ BRAINED	◊ RIFLE	◊ WATCHING
◊ CAGE	◊ SEED	◊ WATER
◊ FEED	◊ SHORE	◊ WATTLE
◊ FRIAR	◊ SNAKE	◊ WHIRLY
◊ HOUSE	◊ SNOW	◊ YARD

```
A M A H S K C A L B E P I K C
E R T T C J P B U S M W F R W
V U Y W T G N S P T I M I A U
O E L A M I O J N K M I R L S
D L I C S A P C W O U L E S T
T E N A L N A U I A W K C H A
I T N M F T K X A O K Y R S F
U A E S L I A V R I Y S O A I
R B T R O B K M H Z S T W W E
F P U A R I P X A N I O N Q L
U E J E I S L D N O Q R C Y D
Y G O L C R E D S I S K I N F
X W A C A M H T N I C A Y H A
I W X K N I G H T J A R S Z R
T O L I M A D O V E Y W C Y E
```

◊ ASH'S LARK

◊ BATELEUR

◊ BLACK SHAMA

◊ FIELDFARE

◊ FIRECROWN

◊ FLORICAN

◊ FRUIT DOVE

◊ GIANT IBIS

◊ HYACINTH MACAW

◊ KAGU

◊ KAKAPO

◊ KIWI

◊ LEAR'S MACAW

◊ LINNET

◊ MALEO

◊ MAO

◊ MILKY STORK

◊ NIGHTJAR

◊ RED SISKIN

◊ SIAU PITTA

◊ SNOWY OWL

◊ TOLIMA DOVE

Bird Profile: Eurasian/Northern Wren

R	E	N	N	I	W	D	F	L	Y	I	N	G	L	S
H	I	G	H	E	R	S	N	E	R	W	V	I	D	G
N	S	T	W	O	O	D	L	A	N	D	G	R	S	N
O	W	N	E	M	U	L	O	V	L	H	I	G	R	I
I	O	W	L	T	S	E	J	A	T	B	N	O	T	P
T	R	O	F	R	P	O	C	E	S	I	U	K	S	P
I	E	R	W	O	Y	I	R	T	L	N	I	R	E	O
T	G	B	R	F	R	D	C	B	D	N	R	A	H	H
E	D	U	U	F	N	E	M	N	G	N	O	S	G	S
P	E	L	A	E	S	E	A	R	N	I	N	G	I	P
M	H	L	L	N	R	B	A	R	R	I	N	G	H	O
O	N	B	I	T	A	I	L	F	O	R	E	S	T	S
C	E	D	E	K	C	O	C	S	S	O	R	C	A	E
O	E	U	N	D	E	R	N	E	A	T	H	S	T	A
J	S	T	A	T	I	B	A	H	E	L	G	A	E	C

Latin Name: *Troglodytes troglodytes*

Family: *Troglodytidae*

Description: A round little bird, the wren is brown all over with lighter parts underneath and some darker barring. It normally holds its tail in a cocked position. They hop and flit about hedgerows foraging for insects, but as they blend in so easily they are often heard but not seen.

Sounds: With its joyful song, it makes up for its size with volume, sometimes trembling with the effort.

Distribution and Habitat: Found across much of Europe and Asia and parts of North Africa, in a range of habitats including shrubland, forests, and woodland.

Fun Fact: In Aesop's fable a competition is held to see which bird can fly the highest. Sitting on the back of an eagle, the wren waits for the eagle to tire, before hopping off and flying a little higher. The wren is declared the winner, thus earning its nickname—the king of birds!

```
E K A N S N W O R B S O P I G
F N V R M G S U D E T O O B O
A N A U P A P X R P B U A L M
B Z J F A Y Y G U O M L M I A
L C V X B V G P N A D E N T R
B C O N G O S E R P E N T T T
B R X E D G L U O A U R Z L I
S O P U O L U G L Y H X R E A
G W Q L I B A T E L E U R E L
U N D S A N F O R D S S E A V
R E C B H N S D E T S E R C T
N D H L L E S S E R F I S H A
E H A A S T S P L M D G X F W
Y O C C U N P E Z Y M G Y P N
S G O K W E S O L I T A R Y Y
```

◊ BALD

◊ BATELEUR

◊ BLACK

◊ BONELLI'S

◊ BOOTED

◊ BROWN
SNAKE

◊ CHACO

◊ CONGO
SERPENT

◊ CRESTED

◊ CROWNED

◊ GOLDEN

◊ GURNEY'S

◊ HAAST'S

◊ HARPY

◊ LESSER FISH

◊ LITTLE

◊ MARTIAL

◊ PAPUAN

◊ PYGMY

◊ SANFORD'S
SEA

◊ SOLITARY

◊ STEPPE

◊ TAWNY

◊ VERREAUX'S

Collared...

```
P N E R W T A N G W F N S T I
U B U S H R O B I N U C E M P
F O R E S T F A L C O N P B X
F R T R E E P I E P O E A T J
B X E L P J L E S C R N T Q K
I T W V H B X O L I T D R R A
R O W G O L W A A S F E A E E
D W C O N L F L H U I G T H B
N H L A R K P R F N R I S C S
O E K I I I I G Y B A N D T O
G E A M G K Y R G I C C E A R
O Q G E E I O W R R A A R C G
R J O W K L J L O D R W L Y V
T N K W A H W O R R A P S L C
W L L E R T E P N F C P I F C
```

- ◊ ANTSHRIKE
- ◊ ARACARI
- ◊ BUSH-ROBIN
- ◊ CROW
- ◊ FALCONET
- ◊ FLYCATCHER
- ◊ FOREST-
  FALCON
- ◊ GNATWREN

- ◊ GROSBEAK
- ◊ IMPERIAL-
  PIGEON
- ◊ INCA
- ◊ LARK
- ◊ LORY
- ◊ OWLET
- ◊ PETREL
- ◊ PLOVER

- ◊ PUFFBIRD
- ◊ REDSTART
- ◊ SCOPS-OWL
- ◊ SPARROW-
  HAWK
- ◊ SUNBIRD
- ◊ TOWHEE
- ◊ TREEPIE
- ◊ TROGON

"Hope" is the thing with feathers by Emily Dickinson

```
C E L V D L U O C W T E U X S
A L P F B U K K Y T N T U S T
A K H O A O X N S U S B P F R
D R A E H S A E T E I O J E A
I R I T M M T W L R T H T X N
L I T T L E J L D S Y S K T G
V G A L E S I N G S U S U R E
S C I W G H Z I L M I S T E S
R R S D C N R S M N D A U M T
E U Y T Z W I D R R R U O I R
H M F E A V N H O M Q H H T E
T B C R R A Z W T Y S O T Y V
A B M S L O Y A S A E R I N E
E E K E P T S U B I U T W B N
F O S D E K S A P E R C H E S
```

"Hope" is the thing with feathers –

That perches in the soul –

And sings the tune without the words –

And never stops – at all –

And sweetest – in the Gale – is heard –

And sore must be the storm –

That could abash the little Bird

That kept so many warm –

I've heard it in the chillest land –

And on the strangest Sea –

Yet – never – in Extremity,

It asked a crumb – of me.

Birds of Asia

```
R E M M I K S K C A L B O E D
W U L I T T L E G R E B E S A
S I A U P I T T A E Z A G P E
R A I N Q U A I L L C U J B H
Y E R P S O M C C L H S N T E
G P O K R E M A H O U U N M L
A M I L K Y S T O R K R K P F
R A W T M S P S X N A F H U F
G L S U O H N S F A R S O N U
A E G W N O O L C I T C R A B
N O A J W K A I N D Q O N I B
E R I D P Q F B Z N R T B B R
Y P U H K G L A P I X E I I A
B C W K M A L L A R D R L S N
K L E R T E P E P A C J L E T
```

◊ ARCTIC LOON

◊ BLACK
  SKIMMER

◊ BRANT

◊ BUFFLEHEAD

◊ CAPE PETREL

◊ CASSOWARY

◊ CHUKAR

◊ GARGANEY

◊ HAMERKOP

◊ HORNBILL

◊ INDIAN
  ROLLER

◊ LITTLE GREBE

◊ MALEO

◊ MALLARD

◊ MILKY STORK

◊ OSPREY

◊ PUNA IBIS

◊ RAIN QUAIL

◊ SIAU PITTA

◊ SNOW DUCK

◊ SURF SCOTER

```
T P U L M D R A Z Z I G T E S
U Y M S A F A A M A M T H W Y
P M U R O K O M S Y I H R N B
A S T V W A Z R A A K D O V I
L C E I M E U J M N B A A E R
O A L T I B I A V E T K T F A
A P T P D E Q F O M D L W E B
Y U T A R Y K S X Q P U E E Z
E L A R Y E U F L A N K L T V
N A W X T S K A T W K L H L L
D R U N R T C I A S Y T Y D A
I W E A P R R L J Y A S P A U
K V T T F I C N D T I E J E C
U Q C H S P F L L I B O R H A
Y P G Q M E N P W I N G T B J
```

◊ BEAK   ◊ FLANK   ◊ RUMP

◊ BELLY   ◊ FOVEA   ◊ SCAPULAR

◊ BILL   ◊ GIZZARD   ◊ TARSUS

◊ BREAST   ◊ HEAD   ◊ THROAT

◊ BURSA   ◊ IRIS   ◊ TIBIA

◊ CLAW   ◊ KIDNEY   ◊ VENT

◊ EYESTRIPE   ◊ MANTLE   ◊ WATTLE

◊ FEET   ◊ MEDULLA   ◊ WING

Bird Profile: California Condor

```
G N I T N U R G P F A P I N K
E C I O V U D R C L I F F Y V
M I L E S R E B M U N U Z L U
E D R L I D O E P I R T S L L
V L E B A R E C X L O R P A T
I I V T S I O E K F F A C C U
T W O S E P C D F Y I P A I R
I R Z T B G O O N R L T P T E
S H O S E R G R S O A O T I S
I W C E G G E N C J C R I R T
U O I R R N R E I T U S V C I
Q L X O A A I A D D U S I B N
N L E F S E O W L I I O T A G
I E M G N I S S I H N L Y L G
B Y D N A L B U R C S G G D C
```

Latin Name: *Gymnogyps californianus*

Family: *Cathartidae*

Description: This largest of the raptors and vultures, the California condor is black all over with a large, white stripe on the underside of its wings. The head is mostly bald and may be pink, orange, or yellow.

Critically endangered, numbers once fell to just 22 birds, all in captivity, but they have recently begun breeding in the wild again. A carrion bird, they soar across the sky, gliding many miles in search of carcasses to feed upon.

Sounds: The California condor does not have a voice box and makes only hissing and grunting sounds.

Distribution and Habitat: Found in parts of the USA and into Mexico in rocky scrubland and forests.

Fun Facts: A lack of predators has made the California condor a bold and inquisitive bird. Highly social and monogamous, they are often seen in pairs, as well as eating and resting near other birds on cliff edges and rocky outcrops.

G	R	E	Y	N	H	C	N	I	F	N	E	E	R	G
G	O	L	D	E	N	F	A	C	E	Z	U	U	Q	H
A	G	E	L	F	F	U	P	G	N	I	W	O	L	G
G	G	E	G	O	O	S	E	O	A	N	W	T	A	G
A	U	K	S	T	A	E	R	G	T	O	L	O	E	M
Y	K	T	E	N	N	A	G	M	T	C	A	M	E	J
E	G	K	W	A	H	S	O	G	I	L	O	E	T	G
N	L	R	E	C	Z	J	Q	R	P	A	R	L	S	O
A	I	L	A	M	O	E	G	E	T	F	E	L	E	L
G	M	U	A	N	G	I	B	B	E	R	B	I	R	D
R	G	X	U	W	D	I	G	E	N	Y	A	U	C	F
A	T	R	G	O	D	A	S	G	R	G	I	G	D	I
G	R	O	U	S	E	A	L	G	A	L	A	H	L	N
T	I	W	D	O	G	Q	G	A	G	M	U	O	O	C
G	G	L	O	S	S	Y	I	B	I	S	G	U	G	H

◊ GADWALL

◊ GALAH

◊ GANNET

◊ GARGANEY

◊ GARNET PITTA

◊ GEOMALIA

◊ GIBBERBIRD

◊ GLOSSY IBIS

◊ GLOWING PUFFLEG

◊ GODWIT

◊ GOLDCREST

◊ GOLDENFACE

◊ GOLDFINCH

◊ GOOSE

◊ GOSHAWK

◊ GRANDALA

◊ GREAT SKUA

◊ GREBE

◊ GREENFINCH

◊ GROUSE

◊ GUACHARO

◊ GUAIABERO

◊ GUILLEMOT

◊ GYRFALCON

Magnificent Migrations

```
S A N D P I P E R L N H E K W
H P W G N I T N U B O R C R O
N A C I L E P B W O L T E H L
V C I D Z L L R K L Q A U T L
S K B A N U Y C O F J M B M A
H C G E B N U P L E M Z D E W
O A D N E C D Y L I O F N J S
V L Z C K E C G N K A I K S P
E B K W R A A G Q E R T C C G
L N A X T E B T K G Z O G Y O
E H G C D I G I E Y C N T A D
R R H L R J R R C R A N E S W
I E A D O H E H A R R I E R I
R B O T S P O O N B I L L D T
Q R W T A O R H T Y B U R W J
```

◊ BALD EAGLE

◊ BEE-EATER

◊ BLACKCAP

◊ BULBUL

◊ BUNTING

◊ CRANES

◊ FLYCATCHER

◊ GODWIT

◊ HARRIER

◊ HAWK-
  CUCKOO

◊ HUMMING-
  BIRD

◊ PELICAN

◊ PEREGRINE

◊ REDPOLL

◊ RUBYTHROAT

◊ SANDPIPER

◊ SHOVELER

◊ SHRIKE

◊ SPOONBILL

◊ STORK

◊ SWALLOW

◊ TERN

◊ WAGTAIL

◊ WRYNECK

Passerines – Part Two

```
N D T W E D G E B I L L D S L
U R C L L I B G N O L B N I J
Y I H S A D D L E B A C K T D
A B A V Y T R D R I B T N A L
L R G E I R E I K A M K O B B
L E R S A T I N B I R D Q E R
E H A S U Q R Y D P Y N S P E
T C U C K O O S H R I K E A L
T T X G S P A R R O W H V C T
I U P U A Q Y J R E O M W Q S
S B A P J G U A H N L E E V I
L O G R U N N E R N T L R F H
L W I F I S C A L G B F I I W
O R I O L E T E V I N I M R V
B O A T B I L L I B N R O H T
```

◊ ANTBIRD

◊ BOATBILL

◊ BOKMAKIERIE

◊ BUTCHER-
  BIRD

◊ CAPE BATIS

◊ CUCKOO-
  SHRIKE

◊ FISCAL

◊ IORA

◊ LOGRUNNER

◊ LONGBILL

◊ MINIVET

◊ ORIOLE

◊ SADDLEBACK

◊ SATINBIRD

◊ SITTELLA

◊ SPARROW

◊ TCHAGRA

◊ THORNBILL

◊ TRILLER

◊ VANGA

◊ VIREO

◊ WEDGEBILL

◊ WHIPBIRD

◊ WHISTLER

Words that Rhyme with SWALLOW

```
W B O T U L P Z O C O M Z I G
O E L Z D X J R P T I M O C P
D L I P U A E V U O N P U E S
U L U I Y Z P W K I M P P E O
H O U D O J B L O E A W W A W
S W I J I P R B T R O M A N K
Y G O U T G R O W L E M K O R
H I T C X Y T D L O O G A T R
W N W E A L L E G R O X D S B
O G N O B L Y E R C O R T E M
D K J U L W L O B L J V W R H
A O I R D L W X H E H O T P O
H O L L O W A B X V L E E Y W
S U A E T A H C E B O X B O W
W A L L O W M V F O L L O W X
```

◊ ALLEGRO   ◊ GIZMO   ◊ PLUTO

◊ BELLOW   ◊ HEDGEROW   ◊ PRESTO

◊ BLOW   ◊ HOLLOW   ◊ SHADOW

◊ BONGO   ◊ METRO   ◊ TEMPO

◊ CALLOW   ◊ MORROW   ◊ VELCRO

◊ CHATEAU   ◊ NOUVEAU   ◊ WALLOW

◊ FOLLOW   ◊ OUTGROW   ◊ YELLOW

◊ GINGKO   ◊ OXBOW   ◊ ZERO

```
S Y G Y G H R H N E N T A E F
N K O R R Y I R U K H O U S E
O S N R E H T R O N S L S K N
W U A L A E O W S S B H T C O
Y D L W T P N U L P E N R E M
B O L D E A R U F O U S A L M
W A E A R S D I H M K B L T O
R L N C B E T U M H B C I T C
Q W T D T Q H E C F R W A I F
W I C T E O A Q R G O E N L J
C H O F R D W U N N W Q Y F B
B P I N T G V A W G N F P W Q
S Z E T H Q J E N A C I R F A
G D N X E V L E Y T N H M I X
X I R E S S E L J K W P A N R
```

◊ AFRICAN   ◊ DUSKY   ◊ NORTHERN

◊ ARCTIC   ◊ EUROPEAN   ◊ PINK

◊ AUSTRALIAN   ◊ GREAT   ◊ RUFOUS

◊ BANDED   ◊ GREEN   ◊ SNOWY

◊ BLACK   ◊ HORNED   ◊ SPOTTED

◊ BLUE   ◊ HOUSE   ◊ WESTERN

◊ BROWN   ◊ LESSER   ◊ WHITE

◊ COMMON   ◊ LITTLE   ◊ YELLOW

Bird Profile: Common Ostrich

```
T D I S T A N C E S T O N E S
L D W H E D I G E S T I O N E
U A O C H V R L E M H P H B L
D E R A S C I P L U M A G E I
A H G E S O I V Y A I L R B M
S S V R A T M R R O T E I S D
R N H D U S R A T U H R T E H
E U A A O D N A L S S A R G M
H R T F B W S K P I O E E E R
T T D R R I N I K S V U T U S
A U E Y O I T Y Y O L S O G D
E O M E P P C A C B Y F R I R
F R O M T J S A T S G E L A I
S D E E P S B U R S T S T N B
S E L B B E P C O M M O N T G
```

Latin Name: *Struthio camelus*

Family: *Struthionidae*

Description: A giant among birds, the male common ostrich can grow to anywhere from 2.1 to 2.8m tall. Males sport black and white plumage while females are a paler brown, and the head is covered in downy feathers. There are four sub-species of common ostrich which are differentiated from the remarkably similar Somali ostrich by their skin tone, common ostriches being pink, Somali ostriches blue. This flightless bird survives its harsh habitat by using its powerful legs to outrun predators. They can maintain high speeds over long distances and in shorter bursts can reach up to 43 miles per hour.

Distribution and Habitat: Found in many parts of Africa often in open habitats such as grassland and semi-desert areas.

Fun Fact: Ostriches do not have teeth and so to aid digestion they eat grit and small pebbles; an adult bird may have up to 1 kg of stones in its digestive system!

```
G S B K C I H C B A D C C Z M
Q L O V E B I R D Y J U T E K
R V B A T E L E U R R I G N G
E P O O R W I L L A L A A L A
L L L I B E O H S R P H T B M
E O I H G C T S R O S A B T E
V R N O A F O A D D V Y E R C
O I K R R W D E E A V E K A O
H K I N G B I R D E K J R J C
S E P B A I N A I A E A R T K
I E R I N H V Y R B C B X H A
W T K L E A T A J A L D E G T
Q T B L Y M P Q R O F L U I O
J C A R D I N A L G J J E N O
U R E K C E P X O C S C G B E
```

◊ AVADAVAT   ◊ CURASSOW   ◊ MEGAPODE

◊ BATELEUR   ◊ DABCHICK   ◊ NIGHTJAR

◊ BEE-EATER   ◊ GAMECOCK   ◊ OXPECKER

◊ BELLBIRD   ◊ GARGANEY   ◊ PARAKEET

◊ BOBOLINK   ◊ HORNBILL   ◊ POORWILL

◊ CARACARA   ◊ KINGBIRD   ◊ REDSHANK

◊ CARDINAL   ◊ LORIKEET   ◊ SHOEBILL

◊ COCKATOO   ◊ LOVEBIRD   ◊ SHOVELER

Ornithologists

```
K S A A B D Y U C S A D W F Q
W C I I G L T A E S P E R K K
X H S O F N M C B A H G E O R
K E N T B A I H U I E Y T E I
C R K A R U C N S U L F S N K
G R A G B S D E N K P L R I S
F I O B I B A U R U S L O G W
B E P R B J O Q S U G L F K O
H O F O Z E K T T A L O Z D R
C F L E M I N G T V Z C D F B
I L G R E K C P E O K I C S M
R N N A M U E N S L E N J M O
D Z Y L D S X P I Z Z E Y A D
L G C L T O K Q X O R X Q H Y
A L L A F P W V O K D A L G P
```

◊ ABBOTT   ◊ FORSTER   ◊ KOZLOVA

◊ ALDRICH   ◊ FRISCH   ◊ KRABBE

◊ CAMARGO   ◊ GADOW   ◊ MCCLURE

◊ CHERRIE   ◊ GLADKOV   ◊ NEUMANN

◊ DOMBROWSKI   ◊ GUNNING   ◊ NICOLL

◊ DUBOIS   ◊ KOENIG   ◊ ODDIE

◊ FALLA   ◊ KOEPCKE   ◊ PHELPS

◊ FLEMING   ◊ KOLLIBAY   ◊ PIZZEY

Humming-Bird by D.H. Lawrence

```
G N I H T Y N A F L A S H E D
B T N H G U O R H T L L L W M
S R R O O H N E E U U T S O E
E H I A I G C N F V T S O F W
S E K L C T E W U I E L U L Y
S A O H L E A U L N S I L O L
O V O U T I D E L W D F L W B
M E L M K B A L R Y R E L E A
O G I M A G I N E C A O O R B
N E R E T T A M C C Z S N S O
S T Q D S D E C R E I P G G R
T A V E N U E S B D L R O W P
E B S M E T S D E P P I H C K
R L D E P S A G A E R O F E B
T E M I T L U C K I L Y G I B
```

I can <u>imagine</u>, in some
   otherworld
Primeval-dumb, far back
In that most <u>awful</u> <u>stillness</u>,
   that only <u>gasped</u> and
   <u>hummed</u>,
Humming-birds <u>raced</u> down
   the <u>avenues</u>.

<u>Before</u> <u>anything</u> had a <u>soul</u>,
While <u>life</u> was a <u>heave</u> of
   <u>Matter</u>, half inanimate,
This <u>little</u> bit <u>chipped</u> off in
   <u>brilliance</u>
And went whizzing <u>through</u>
   the <u>slow</u>, vast, succulent
   <u>stems</u>.

I <u>believe</u> there were no
   <u>flowers</u>, then
In the <u>world</u> where the
   humming-bird <u>flashed</u>
   ahead of <u>creation</u>.
I believe he <u>pierced</u> the slow
   <u>vegetable</u> veins with his
   long <u>beak</u>.
<u>Probably</u> he was <u>big</u>.

As <u>mosses</u>, and little <u>lizards</u>,
   they <u>say</u> were <u>once</u> big.
Probably he was a jabbing,
   terrifying <u>monster</u>.
We <u>look</u> at him through the
   <u>wrong</u> end of the <u>long</u>
   telescope of <u>Time</u>,
<u>Luckily</u> for us.

Birds of Oceania

```
L L I B N O O P S L A Y O R S
B L A C K S W A N P Y Z U B O
K A H A R C R V K X T M Y I O
G R J S K K T E K G E R E T T
L R M S Y A I M E I H T R C Y
O U H O M Q K N L D W R P Z T
S B C W R N N A G W L I S J E
S A N A B E E I P F G L O L R
Y K I R O T P B L O I A I P N
I O F Y Y G U O P N Y S L K H
B O A E Z P V X R I U E H A V
I K R H A S I Q J K B D M E H
S G B Q K S I L V E R E Y E R
U R E J E G R E A T E G R E T
O S Z C A P E G A N N E T V Z
```

◊ BLACK SWAN   ◊ GREAT EGRET   ◊ KOOKABURRA

◊ CAPE GANNET   ◊ GREY TEAL   ◊ MOREPORK

◊ CASSOWARY   ◊ KAKAPO   ◊ OSPREY

◊ DUNLIN   ◊ KEA   ◊ ROYAL
                                   SPOONBILL

◊ EMU   ◊ KILLDEER
                                 ◊ SILVEREYE
◊ GALAH   ◊ KINGFISHER
                                 ◊ SOOTY TERN
◊ GLOSSY IBIS   ◊ KIWI
                                 ◊ ZEBRA FINCH

```
K W A H H S I F I W E B E R G
R A Z O R B I L L S O X H K P
G C Y S F R I G A T E B I R D
R E T O C S K S E A E A G L E
J N L T R O P I C B I R D T J
O A T E R R U M T G A N N E T
G C N I F F U P U T O N U Y S
U I A R F L L X N D I S A S I
I L R A T U C E D I U W O Q R
L E O T E P L Y R Z U R A R C
L P M L I D S M B T T G D K O
E B R R G A S O A A E Y N C E
M T O D Y K O K B R H P P E T
O P C S U B I L T E L K U A P
T A D A Y F A I R Y P R I O N
```

◊ ALBATROSS   ◊ GANNET   ◊ PETREL

◊ AUKLET   ◊ GREBE   ◊ PUFFIN

◊ BOOBY   ◊ GUILLEMOT   ◊ RAZORBILL

◊ CORMORANT   ◊ KITTIWAKE   ◊ SCOTER

◊ FAIRY PRION   ◊ MURRE   ◊ SEA EAGLE

◊ FISH HAWK   ◊ NODDY   ◊ SKUA

◊ FRIGATEBIRD   ◊ PELICAN   ◊ TERN

◊ FULMAR   ◊ PENGUIN   ◊ TROPICBIRD

```
S I D N D E T A L L E C O A M
W W X N Z B R N J L Q H U O T
A W F A D I P N A T O G O B X
M O A M K L O R D H O W E N J
P O R A A V T G L A Y S A N O
H D M D K S N O I N U E R K K
E H A N U I Z E Z U P I K C I
N E K A R C E L T T I L F O N
E N G O X Q S U C E T Z A C A
R U N J N N T N A B V W D R W
A S L Y I V P I L T H P W E A
C T S W A V A L A K A S K T Z
S G E O I J F L Y D U A L A T
A L M K R B G A A L J I H W T
M E F Z H A U G N E L U K N R
```

◊ ANDAMAN

◊ AUSTRAL

◊ AZTEC

◊ BOGOTA

◊ CALAYAN

◊ GALLINULE

◊ LAYSAN

◊ LEWIN'S

◊ LITTLE CRAKE

◊ LORD HOWE

◊ MAKIRA

◊ MASCARENE

◊ NKULENGU

◊ OCELLATED

◊ OKINAWA

◊ REUNION

◊ SAKALAVA

◊ SNORING

◊ SORA

◊ SWAMPHEN

◊ TALAUD

◊ WATERCOCK

◊ WEKA

◊ WOODHEN

Bird Profile:
Marabou Stork

```
N D N Q A W D E V I S S A M R
E T L S U N B U R N E D B P D
C Y S A U I I I Q A A G S O N
K P D O B N E M R I C N T U A
A I F T U H U T A D R I O C L
P C K F J N D S H L O T R H S
P A W U S A D C U L S R K F S
E L E T P S A S O A S I D J A
A U T A A E K N B C L U E S R
R O L L R P G I Y K G Q S E G
A B A L C N L L N I T S S P U
N A N O S L E S G N I W I O L
C R D O I G Z D M G Y F M H A
E A S C S U N D E R T A K E R
A M E T H O D S T A T I B A H
```

Latin Name: *Leptoptilos crumenifer*

Family: *Ciconiidae*

Description: This colonial bird is not easily missed at up to 1.5m tall with a massive wingspan which can reach up to 2.9m. It has a bald, pink head and neck that appear sunburned, black cape-like wings, a white tuft at the neck, and a pink gular pouch, all atop long, skinny legs. Sometimes described as unusual or macabre-looking, it has earned the nickname the "undertaker bird". Indeed, it is often found lurking near carrion killed by other animals in opportunistic hopes of scavenging the scraps.

Sounds: Lacking a voice box, it is, as is typical with storks, a quiet bird. It makes some sounds using its throat pouch and by clattering its massive dagger-like bill.

Distribution and Habitat: Found across much of sub-Saharan Africa in a variety of habitats such as grassland and wetlands.

Fun Fact: The marabou stork has an unusual method of keeping cool… squirting excrement down its legs, giving them their white appearance.

```
V Y R A W O S S A C U N E T Y
D Y E K R U T U T O A Q C E I
G A S T O R N I S C Q S S R N
K E L E N K E N I S V I T R D
K H A Y R J P L S J B N O O I
O A A O V B E S T I W R C R A
R O T A M P O C D O E O O B N
I S S S S R T E H P T T T I P
B N C T T T T I M W H N O R E
U E J A R S S E T V D O U D A
S E B I E I W E B A O R C S F
T L M R K I C A A Q N B A H O
A Q C U N K V H N G A I N F W
R J H S I N R O I V L Y S A L
D A S O R N I S U J T E Q L G
```

◊ ALBATROSS

◊ BRONTORNIS

◊ CASSOWARY

◊ CRESTED IBIS

◊ DASORNIS

◊ EMPEROR

◊ EMU

◊ GASTORNIS

◊ HAAST'S EAGLE

◊ INDIAN PEAFOWL

◊ KELENKEN

◊ KORI BUSTARD

◊ MOA

◊ OSTRICH

◊ PELICAN

◊ STORK

◊ SWAN

◊ SYLVIORNIS

◊ TERROR BIRDS

◊ TITANIS

◊ TOCO TOUCAN

◊ TURKEY

```
W O L B M L O W W O Z D G E O
S A W O T P M O G I T R E V E
B K R C T F A L K G A J O Y M
E S C R O W N L Y W W O F K O
O N I M O D Y A O C I L A C R
H T R B C W D F T R F A W X N
G F W W I Q A D A G I O I P E
U W O O T U S S G C A W O O S
O J X N R M E Z L P S L T I W
H G O N O R V S O U I E O T O
T H W I P C W L W T L O R A L
L E N M A A I H I T L I A P L
A L I M X O T C S U Z G T L E
I L E J W H O I O I D U A O B
J O W S F E M E W O B B H L W
```

◊ ADAGIO   ◊ CAMEO   ◊ MISTLETOE

◊ AGLOW   ◊ DOMINO   ◊ PATIO

◊ ALTHOUGH   ◊ DYNAMO   ◊ POLIO

◊ ARROW   ◊ ESCROW   ◊ POLITICO

◊ AUDIO   ◊ FALLOW   ◊ PORTICO

◊ BELLOW   ◊ HELLO   ◊ ROMEO

◊ BLOW   ◊ IMPRESARIO   ◊ TAROT

◊ CALICO   ◊ MINNOW   ◊ VERTIGO

```
F B K N E S A A C N I T W H K
R A Y M O B D I O B I L B F R
N R D K P A L L I D S W L W H
A T A G S W D V C A E O E S S
I A S R O U N A O Z U N E A J
E I R N B O D S N U G G D G M
L L S E M E D Y D E I A I N O
T E A E R I Z T B R R A N U U
R D L H A F U T X O D G G Y R
U P I M Y Y P D A R O J H R N
T W O L K M I N D O R O E R I
R N R U A N D A M A N Z A O N
D W Y E M M Q B O T Q W R C G
T R O C A Z O S H I L L T K O
X X E V I L O S O R O M O C R
```

◊ ANDAMAN

◊ AZUERO

◊ BAR-TAILED

◊ BLEEDING-
  HEART

◊ COMOROS
  OLIVE

◊ DIAMOND

◊ DUSKY

◊ GRENADA

◊ HILL

◊ INCA

◊ LEMON

◊ MINDORO

◊ MOURNING

◊ PALLID

◊ ROCK

◊ RODRIGUES

◊ RYUKYU

◊ SNOW

◊ SOMALI

◊ TROCAZ

◊ TURTLE

◊ WONGA

◊ YUNGAS

◊ ZEBRA

```
V R I O L I F T E E K A R A P
R A I N B O W L O R Y D U C K
U G Z E B R A F I N C H T O N
S I N O E G I P E V E O Z C W
U R C V Z C O K L J R S X K H
L E I T A K C O C R U C E A A
A G W I P I R C A N N M X T L
H D Q J H I T P O Q O M H O A
P U J C I G L I T H C K Q O G
E B K N O A P H C N I F L W O
C V I O G S O N G C A N A R Y
I V S E P S I T T A C U L A P
O E N J E F L O V E B I R D Z
P E V A S A P A R R O T L E T
S R G A W R J A L L E S O R S
```

◊ BUDGERIGAR   ◊ LORIINI   ◊ PSITTACULA

◊ CAIQUE   ◊ LOVEBIRD   ◊ RAINBOW
                                      LORY
◊ CHICKEN   ◊ OWL FINCH
                                    ◊ ROSELLA
◊ COCKATIEL   ◊ PARAKEET
                                    ◊ SENEGAL
◊ COCKATOO   ◊ PARROTLET   PARROT

◊ CONURE   ◊ PIGEON   ◊ SONG
                                      CANARY
◊ DUCK   ◊ PIONUS
                                    ◊ VASA PARROT
◊ GALAH   ◊ POICEPHALUS
                                    ◊ ZEBRA FINCH
◊ GOOSE

```
E E O P O O H D O O W O L S T
W P N D G F I G B I R D L L I
K Y T N R T C O C H O A L W M
Y G A K H I E F G W K A I O R
A M V R X C B B M F L R A F E
M Y A A S A W R R L J A T E H
A G D C Y T S S E A P C N L B
N O A Q P B N S L K B A R G E
A O V U T I O Y V D N R O N E
K S A E C R O M B E C I H U E
I E H T F D S R R M F Y T J A
N I D T P E A F O W L D M C T
V O Q A K I N G F I S H E R E
K R K I E B R O A D B I L L R
L A C L R E P I P D N A S F C
```

◊ ARACARI

◊ AVADAVAT

◊ BARBET

◊ BEE-EATER

◊ BROADBILL

◊ CATBIRD

◊ COCHOA

◊ CROMBEC

◊ FIGBIRD

◊ HERMIT

◊ HYLIA

◊ IORA

◊ JUNGLEFOWL

◊ KINGFISHER

◊ MANAKIN

◊ MANGO

◊ PEAFOWL

◊ PYGMY-
GOOSE

◊ RACQUET-
TAIL

◊ ROSELLA

◊ SANDPIPER

◊ THORNTAIL

◊ TINKERBIRD

◊ WOOD
HOOPOE

Bird Profile: Wandering Albatross

```
W I N G S P A N B E T W E E N
Y G R S S O R T A B L A F T W
T R J U V E N I L E S I M O O
E U B S H I P S L C S A R N R
I N A L O N G K I H S S E N B
R T K E A F S R V S R E T A W
A S D N D C C E I D N H A C S
V Y A S O L K V N O P C I R M
E S E L E W E E G O I T N E A
G S T E M I N N I F N A I T E
A U S V I A W N E E K P N I R
M F N A T A T D E E R B G H C
U I I R S N R E H T U O S W S
L N T T E D I S R E D N U A Q
P G E O R G I A I R B O R N E
```

Latin Name: *Diomedea exulans*

Family: *Diomedeidae*

Description: The plumage varies greatly, with juveniles starting brown and becoming whiter as they age, retaining some dark patches or "dirty" markings. The underside of the wing is white with black tips, and tails are often black. They have large, pink bills and feet and the largest wingspan of any living bird, up to 3.5m across. They circle the entire globe on their travels, their massive wings allowing them to stay airborne for hours at a time without even flapping.

Sounds: The wandering albatross has a variety of vocalizations including grunts and screams.

Distribution and Habitat: Ranging the southern oceans between sub-tropical and sub-Antarctic waters. They breed on South Georgia.

Fun Fact: Though they normally fish for food, they are not fussy eaters—they've been known to follow ships looking for waste, gorging themselves to the point that they cannot fly and instead just bob along on the water.

```
D P E R T A I N E M E E U B G
D S Q N F Q I Y E N E Y N X Y
N P L B G A O M A Y A I C D H
F I P L L A B L E S A V O B N
T L A P E R P S Y H P C C I C
K Z M R A X T M C W A A A O C
N O N N B R P F A M S M I W U
C I E I A X W L P H E N N N E
C T A I A F T A A R C I E E N
R O N T A R I X K I Y A X N A
W E G U N G F H C H N R L A F
W J G I N I J E B K F G S B O
X O A A Q U A T R A I N J R R
L R E L I O L M T W A I N U P
D Z O C F N I A R E Z U S N O
```

◊ BRAIN   ◊ EYESTRAIN   ◊ REFRAIN

◊ CAMPAIGN   ◊ INGRAIN   ◊ REGAIN

◊ CHAIN   ◊ MAINTAIN   ◊ REMAIN

◊ CHAMPAGNE   ◊ MEMBRANE   ◊ SPAIN

◊ COCAINE   ◊ PERTAIN   ◊ SUZERAIN

◊ COMPLAIN   ◊ PLANE   ◊ TWAIN

◊ DRAIN   ◊ PROFANE   ◊ URBANE

◊ EXPLAIN   ◊ QUATRAIN   ◊ VANE

```
K Q A O M T N A I G J N N S I
C A M P B E L L T E A L I G S
K X D G C D O D O K K B U H O
E U C I W A S O E A I E G O M
R G A A Z U W W G R L A N L A
K N S N E C N U E E S B E A L
V E S T H K V T P M N A P N I
K G O C A L P H R U I S S A O
T U W O K A A Z M S P P U O S
D D A O A N M I G A E H R M T
M V R T T D O P I W R J F C R
J A Y B A T N N B W A O Z A I
C L I A R E L B I S I V N I C
S R E A W A R G E Y L K U L H
D E T S W L F G O P A K A K J
```

◊ APTERIBIS

◊ AUCKLAND
   TEAL

◊ CAMPBELL
   TEAL

◊ CASSOWARY

◊ DODO

◊ ELEPHANT
   BIRD

◊ EMU

◊ GIANT COOT

◊ GIANT MOA

◊ GREAT AUK

◊ INVISIBLE
   RAIL

◊ KAGU

◊ KAKAPO

◊ KIWI

◊ MOA-NALO

◊ PENGUIN

◊ RHEA

◊ SNIPE-RAIL

◊ SOMALI
   OSTRICH

◊ TAKAHE

◊ WEKA

The Owl by Alfred, Lord Tennyson

```
M  G  S  D  I  A  M  K  L  I  M  Q  N  B  I
F  N  G  H  C  D  G  N  I  R  R  I  H  W  M
A  I  O  R  R  J  N  T  Y  D  K  N  S  S  Z
U  M  J  Y  A  O  H  U  H  R  L  X  T  U  E
E  R  T  B  U  R  U  H  O  C  F  O  A  N  H
H  A  M  H  I  E  E  N  M  R  E  L  C  G  N
L  W  S  C  G  V  A  L  D  A  G  T  E  I  W
A  W  E  T  S  I  S  L  Y  E  E  H  I  B  O
T  S  O  S  H  F  L  M  O  Y  L  R  S  H  M
C  A  G  T  Y  A  A  B  E  N  E  A  T  H  W
H  I  P  I  O  R  T  E  W  L  E  M  Y  S  E
S  L  C  S  C  O  R  C  M  C  L  T  B  D  N
O  T  J  S  J  F  X  E  H  O  D  S  V  U  U
C  L  I  C  K  F  Q  A  M  C  C  E  H  M  K
E  C  I  W  T  F  Y  D  W  K  Y  D  W  B  Y
```

When cats run home and light is come,

And dew is cold upon the ground,

And the far-off stream is dumb,

And the whirring sail goes round,

And the whirring sail goes round;

Alone and warming his five wits,

The white owl in the belfry sits.

When merry milkmaids click the latch,

And rarely smells the new-mown hay,

And the cock hath sung beneath the thatch

Twice or thrice his roundelay,

Twice or thrice his roundelay;

Alone and warming his five wits,

The white owl in the belfry sits.

Birdwatching in Serengeti National Park

```
O X G T E R G E T A E R G U H
B L A C K K I T E B R S Y Z O
W T V L W N I T R A M K C O R
Q U L W H I M B R E L T I W U
T F I W S E N I P L A R Y H S
M A C C O A D U C K O E E D S
A T A H C N I H W A R E N H W
F L W O H S R A M P Y P A A I
O F C N S W S A S C J I G M F
X U R B U R B O B B P P R E T
Y E P I N S K C A J N I A R F
L N Y A N Z A S W I F T G K F
A F R I C A N C R A K E E O U
R U A J C A P E C R O W D P R
K W A H T A B B A T E L E U R
```

◊ AFRICAN CRAKE

◊ ALPINE SWIFT

◊ BARN OWL

◊ BAT HAWK

◊ BATELEUR

◊ BLACK KITE

◊ BRUBRU

◊ CAPE CROW

◊ FOXY LARK

◊ GARGANEY

◊ GREAT EGRET

◊ HAMERKOP

◊ HORUS SWIFT

◊ JACK SNIPE

◊ MACCOA DUCK

◊ MARSH OWL

◊ NYANZA SWIFT

◊ OSPREY

◊ ROCK MARTIN

◊ RUFF

◊ SHIKRA

◊ TREE PIPIT

◊ WHIMBREL

◊ WHINCHAT

Little… – Part Two

```
L  I  A  R  D  O  O  W  J  R  B  H  I  Z  L
O  T  R  E  T  A  E  E  E  B  N  I  U  Z  L
D  N  V  T  H  O  R  N  B  I  R  D  P  L  W
D  A  S  H  E  A  R  W  A  T  E  R  Q  O  O
W  R  P  T  I  W  I  K  D  E  T  T  O  P  S
A  O  I  H  E  R  M  I  T  M  T  F  F  T  I
C  M  B  B  T  N  E  V  A  R  I  K  Z  E  H
A  R  L  P  S  M  E  D  L  C  B  N  R  E  T
M  O  U  G  X  S  S  I  R  R  G  W  U  K  I
E  C  E  R  E  V  A  E  W  A  G  P  C  I  C
U  B  H  Z  L  T  S  R  M  K  T  Q  N  R  U
L  V  E  K  K  C  V  T  G  E  V  S  V  O  C
B  E  R  R  F  P  M  M  I  A  A  G  U  L  K
A  X  O  R  G  G  R  E  E  N  B  U  L  B  O
J  F  N  P  I  W  G  G  N  I  T  N  U  B  O
```

◊ BEE-EATER

◊ BITTERN

◊ BLUE HERON

◊ BLUE MACAW

◊ BUNTING

◊ BUSTARD

◊ CORMORANT

◊ CRAKE

◊ CUCKOO

◊ FORKTAIL

◊ GRASSBIRD

◊ GREBE

◊ GREENBUL

◊ HERMIT

◊ LORIKEET

◊ OWL

◊ RAVEN

◊ SHEARWATER

◊ SPOTTED
KIWI

◊ STINT

◊ TERN

◊ THORNBIRD

◊ WEAVER

◊ WOOD-RAIL

Bird Profile: House Sparrow

```
J G N I G N I S A T R E T A W
X C N W F F I N D I C A T E D
Y H U I P L L A M S E C N E F
L A T B H U H U M A N O I S Y
L T S L E T E S K E E H C U N
A T U P A T A C S Y K Q Z O E
R E D Y A E D B N O P C H H E
U R P F L R W C A A C R O S S
T I C A A I R W O C D I I L V
A N U E N N T O S N K N A H F
N G H B N G U T W E I C U L C
G Y T E I R A V E S V C A B D
B E N E F I T S T R N A A L A
K R E N I A L P E O P L E L B
G L O B E S H O R T N E V I L
```

Latin Name: *Passer domesticus*

Family: *Passeridae*

Description: A small bird, the male has a red-brown nape and back, white cheeks, pale undersides, a black bib, and wings prettily patterned with a variety of browns. The females are plainer and paler. Both have short, squared tails and stout, conical beaks. They can be spotted fluttering in and out of the eaves of buildings and hopping along fences. A social bird, they are often seen in groups singing or bathing, in either dust or water.

Sounds: House sparrows can be noisy and may be heard chattering away in a short and chirpy song as they flock together.

Distribution and Habitat: Found across much of the globe both naturally and introduced.

Fun Facts: As indicated by the word "house" in their name, they are rarely found away from human settlements, choosing to live alongside people for the wealth of benefits that brings, such as an abundance of food.

Red-billed...

```
T M A L K O H A D H Y P F G L
O F R A N C O L I N F P J N L
R O X K K W A C H O U G H I I
R X T P A R T R I D G E Q L B
A P M Y E P G V F T W H U R E
P E I M R L A I N O G Q A A H
G C E G L A R R S Z D M I T T
N K K D E E N S R B B C L S Y
I E R S F O A N N O X Q F A C
G R W I H R N B U F T O I L S
N U N Q U E L E A L I S N L H
A C N C T O U C A N E K C U D
H L L I B N R O H M K T H G V
D W A R F H O R N B I L L Y A
S C I M I T A R B A B B L E R
```

◊ CHOUGH

◊ CURASSOW

◊ DUCK

◊ DWARF
  HORNBILL

◊ EMERALD

◊ FIREFINCH

◊ FRANCOLIN

◊ GULL

◊ HANGING-
  PARROT

◊ HORNBILL

◊ MALKOHA

◊ MESIA

◊ OXPECKER

◊ PARROT

◊ PARTRIDGE

◊ PIGEON

◊ QUAILFINCH

◊ QUELEA

◊ SCIMITAR-
  BABBLER

◊ SCYTHEBILL

◊ STARLING

◊ TOUCAN

◊ TYRANNULET

```
R I H Y A C I N T H M A C A W
L E H A R P Y E A G L E Y A H
X A I K R T F I W S E S U O H
H I E R R D H E A E O S E H A
O H H T R A H Y H T P N A O N
R N E H T A L E M X O R I A T
N E R R A O H S A S O P U T F
E R R W E W T C E D H G Q Z I
D W I J H R F N I M D U J I W
C Y N I Y P O I E E U H I N S
O P G F B A D C N T M H H A S
O P G M B H M R H C T A H H U
T A U H O Y O A U A H O W H R
G H L A H H W H A L T B H H O
H I L N I K S I S D E D O O H
```

◊ HAPPY WREN

◊ HARDHEAD

◊ HARPY EAGLE

◊ HARRIER

◊ HAWFINCH

◊ HAWK

◊ HERERO CHAT

◊ HERRING GULL

◊ HOATZIN

◊ HOBBY

◊ HOODED SISKIN

◊ HOOPOE

◊ HORNED COOT

◊ HORNED GUAN

◊ HORUS SWIFT

◊ HOTTENTOT TEAL

◊ HOUSE SWIFT

◊ HUIA

◊ HUME'S LARK

◊ HWAMEI

◊ HYACINTH MACAW

Words that Rhyme with CRAKE

```
E K A T P A K E X I N T A K E
G J E E K A R W E K A M N U H
I D K N A M E S A K E P C P C
E W A K E J O E T E D W H V A
X K W I S H E I K A G E C E H
K E A S D L A A K A K H T K T
A E E B K T T B V E T E D A O
E P K O E E F A C E G R H H O
R S A A R L G C H U E C E S T
B A R T S B W K K Q P G A V S
Y K D C R R C A E A E C D N O
A E Z A X R E C C P J L A K E
D C K K S T Z H I O K K C K N
G E H E S B E E N K E E H L E
C U S L A K E K A S E S E N Y
```

◊ AWAKE	◊ INTAKE	◊ SHAKE
◊ BACKACHE	◊ KEEPSAKE	◊ SHEIK
◊ BAKE	◊ LAKE	◊ SLAKE
◊ BRAKE	◊ NAMESAKE	◊ SNAKE
◊ CUPCAKE	◊ OATCAKE	◊ STAKE
◊ DAYBREAK	◊ OPAQUE	◊ STEAK
◊ DRAKE	◊ OVERTAKE	◊ TOOTHACHE
◊ HEADACHE	◊ RETAKE	◊ UNMAKE

```
L V A F L A M I N G O L P H T
K N N W M E L A M P I T T A B
T C A H P H X R T E P L U N R
B O C U J R N E L A E N I A U
F U A G Y O L N U D T B H S G
I C J Q T N U N I L K C O G N
S A Y H E V O U S L N Y R E I
H L U E K D G R M I K E N L W
E R R E D Y K D F O Y U E W T
A G O Y E E O A O S O Q R O R
G H T N S B O O H O H R O L O
L N O T J K M R Y T K N H L H
E H R N A C I R O L F C P E S
G E E D A K S I K E O U U Y N
L Z S E E D C R A C K E R C K
```

◊ COUCAL   ◊ GREY SHRIKE   ◊ MELAMPITTA

◊ CUCKOO   ◊ HONEYGUIDE   ◊ MOORHEN

◊ ELAENIA   ◊ HORNERO   ◊ NODDY

◊ FISH EAGLE   ◊ JACANA   ◊ NOTHURA

◊ FLAMINGO   ◊ KESTREL   ◊ RHEA

◊ FLORICAN   ◊ KISKADEE

◊ GREENLET   ◊ KOA FINCH

Collective Nouns

```
P A L L I T O L F N H A P H H
Y R A D I A N C E E A S U T Y
S D A I N R B W U S L D U G D
L U T W U O P T Y W D T P L M
U K M R E F I L D L X O T S F
R K D R E N U T E A O T U A S
P E A G N M O L A C M R D S R
P P M J A J B I S T I W E C E
U B R M C T K L S X N N Q O T
E A A R I B B N I N D E U R S
C T H E T H J I I N E T M R U
N T C W A S S E I Q G C W A M
A E Y T V P M K K X F Q S L L
D R Q I Z S N S E T T E L A P
A Y K W N U D P X S P A R T Y
```

◊ ASCENSION   ◊ FLUSH   ◊ SCOOP

◊ ASYLUM   ◊ HUDDLE   ◊ SHIMMER

◊ BATTERY   ◊ LAMENTATION   ◊ SKEIN

◊ CHARM   ◊ MUSTER   ◊ SLURP

◊ CORRAL   ◊ PALETTE   ◊ TREMBLING

◊ DANCE   ◊ PARTY   ◊ UNKINDNESS

◊ DECEIT   ◊ RADIANCE   ◊ VATICAN

◊ FLOTILLA   ◊ RATTLE   ◊ WARP

Bird Derived Last Names

```
H I A E G L Y R U R U K R K N
D N I L W V N L E E E S X U T
R T F I W S J V I L G K W H F
I V N I T R A M V P D F L A I
B C U L V E R A H S M A O W N
U N E R W P V O G E L D K K C
K N X I Q H E R O N C I O U H
C P R L U N M A F T X R S N Z
O N F Q I T L A C A X Z A F I
C D O X Z V P Y R O L X W N A
D T W Q A M S E L O C C S F E
O K L A C G M V D F K K O J K
O A E L A G N I T H G I N N O
W E R P W W O L L A W S S B G
Q W J L G C E G D I R T R A P
```

◊ ADLER   ◊ HAWK   ◊ SOKOL

◊ AMSEL   ◊ HERON   ◊ SWALLOW

◊ BIRD   ◊ MARTIN   ◊ SWAN

◊ CRANE   ◊ NIGHTINGALE   ◊ SWIFT

◊ CULVER   ◊ PARTRIDGE   ◊ VOGEL

◊ FALCON   ◊ PEACOCK   ◊ WEAVER

◊ FINCH   ◊ PHOENIX   ◊ WOODCOCK

◊ FOWLER   ◊ SIKORA   ◊ WREN

Bird Profile: Gouldian Finch

```
T C H E S T V A R I E D Y M I
Y D Q E G T R G Y E Q L H I D
P D E O H A O S R A L G O X G
E D I R I U R T E E M T L E R
S D O N L S R O B D N E L D A
V A B D S T E Y F A P C O Y S
T O I P S R S E I A B R W H S
W A S V P A U L N M R G S B L
N M I M A L L L D A E H O T A
Y F M E H I T O B S E B G D N
L L I M R A E W R W D D N F D
I U L B E R D D I O I I I S
M F A E P C U Y G H N V T N D
A F R R D E E F H S G I A C I
F S E S T C A R T T A V M H B
```

Latin Name: *Chloebia gouldiae*

Family: *Estrildidae*

Description: Unmistakable due to its vivid plumage, the Gouldian finch has a yellow belly, purple chest, black throat, green back, and blue nape. Its face is yellow, black, or red. Though females are less bright than their male counterparts, they are otherwise similar in appearance.

Like many members of the finch family, they feed on seeds, for which they forage. Outside the breeding season they may be seen in mixed flocks with other types of finches. During the mating season, the male fluffs his feathers and bobs his head in a bid to attract a mate as he shows off his brilliant feathers.

Distribution and habitat: The Gouldian finch lives in tree hollows on shrubland and grasslands in parts of northern Australia.

Fun Fact: Perhaps unsurprisingly, the varied and vivid feathers of the Gouldian finch have resulted in the alternative name, the rainbow finch.

```
F M V N A C I L E P M L T K X
X E Q B A B B L E R U N E A B
L S F U L V E T T A S Y B K U
L I V R A J T H G I N R R O S
I T X S M I T O F G A O A O H
B E W R A K L T L H K L B B W
T E J N B G W L C K E E N O A
O L S V B I R N U R E Q R O R
R O R H N L I E G O A M O B B
R I E S R F F O P A G H T O L
A R P C E I S L C E L N N O E
P O P R R H K N P C E A E B R
T J I B A A I E N V M R C Y N
B F D W Q E K J R A M A C A J
W T K C Z P P E V L I F A P P
```

◊ ACCENTOR   ◊ DIPPER   ◊ NIGHTJAR

◊ BABBLER   ◊ FIREFINCH   ◊ ORIOLE

◊ BARBET   ◊ FULVETTA   ◊ PARROTBILL

◊ BOOBOOK   ◊ GOSHAWK   ◊ PELICAN

◊ BOOBY   ◊ INCA   ◊ QUAIL

◊ BUSH WARBLER   ◊ JACAMAR   ◊ SHRIKE

◊ CRAKE   ◊ LORY   ◊ SNAKE EAGLE

◊ CREEPER   ◊ MESITE   ◊ TWINSPOT

```
C O P E P T E R Y X I P P L U
B A A R G E N T A V I S D S Y
S O C A H R S U R O H P I I A
X Y U V A O M T N A I G H N D
I C A D Y P T E S D B S C R Z
O Y O P H Y S O R N I S R O E
O D T A E P Y O R N I S A T B
O K W E K F M B R L W F D N I
A N T H R O P O R N I S H O L
Z N P K R A L J T N X C Z R L
K S I N R O T S A G B N A B S
L D I S I N R O K C O L L U B
A S I A N O S T R I C H K T E
B K F Q P A O M D N A L P U M
K E L E N K E N T I T A N I S
```

◊ ADZEBILL

◊ AEPYORNIS

◊ AIOLORNIS

◊ ANTHRO-
  PORNIS

◊ ARGENTAVIS

◊ ASIAN
  OSTRICH

◊ AZHDARCHID

◊ BRONTORNIS

◊ BULLOCK-
  ORNIS

◊ COPEPTERYX

◊ DODO

◊ DROMORNIS

◊ GASTORNIS

◊ GIANT MOA

◊ ICADYPTES

◊ KELENKEN

◊ PHORUS-
  RHACOS

◊ PHYSORNIS

◊ TERATORN

◊ TITANIS

◊ UPLAND MOA

```
B U S A R W R E L B B A B E B
L A C U O C Y A B R A W O N A
D R I B K C A L B C O R A H B
B U L L F I N C H R B W B L R
B A T H A W K B C O S T U E B
B O B U O B U I R S I E K O T
R H U X E Z A E K T T W B B R
A E J S Z G A C E H A O I U E
M B R A G L I U R H L I T S N
B A R N O W L O D I W V T T I
L D A W E B A E N E B A E A M
I B L B M T R K R E T Z R R L
N P B E A R D E D T I T N D L
G A R Y A E L G A E D L A B E
D R I B E U L B R O L G A T B
```

◊ BABBLER

◊ BALD EAGLE

◊ BANGGAI
  CROW

◊ BARBET

◊ BARN OWL

◊ BARRED
  HAWK

◊ BAT HAWK

◊ BAY COUCAL

◊ BEARDED TIT

◊ BELL MINER

◊ BESRA

◊ BEWICK'S
  SWAN

◊ BITTERN

◊ BLACKBIRD

◊ BLUEBIRD

◊ BLUETHROAT

◊ BLUETIT

◊ BOBOLINK

◊ BOREAL OWL

◊ BRAMBLING

◊ BROLGA

◊ BULLFINCH

◊ BUSTARD

◊ BUZZARD

A	S	E	P	T	R	E	K	C	E	P	D	O	O	W
C	U	L	B	L	E	V	S	Y	A	P	H	U	I	A
R	U	O	T	L	Z	C	E	O	O	O	R	A	D	B
O	N	R	C	I	H	R	O	T	O	A	M	R	Y	L
S	I	B	L	B	E	O	V	V	U	G	I	A	G	A
S	F	T	Y	E	G	I	R	W	A	B	N	C	Z	C
B	F	O	E	O	W	O	F	N	G	S	A	A	F	K
I	U	U	U	H	E	L	D	N	B	E	C	R	I	S
L	P	C	E	S	A	K	I	W	I	I	I	I	N	K
L	C	A	F	M	G	M	E	S	I	H	L	X	C	I
C	E	N	I	R	M	S	S	N	E	T	E	L	H	M
N	A	N	N	U	S	T	F	A	J	B	P	L	U	M
F	G	E	H	S	P	O	O	N	B	I	L	L	S	E
O	L	L	I	B	R	O	Z	A	R	Z	R	C	R
U	E	M	F	I	S	K	E	R	U	T	L	U	V	E

◊ AVOCET

◊ BALD EAGLE

◊ BLACK SKIMMER

◊ CANADA GOOSE

◊ COLLARED ARACARI

◊ CRESTED COUA

◊ CROSSBILL

◊ DALMATIAN PELICAN

◊ FINCH

◊ FLAMINGO

◊ GODWIT

◊ GREAT HORNBILL

◊ HUIA

◊ KEEL-BILLED TOUCAN

◊ KING VULTURE

◊ KIWI

◊ LONG-BILLED CURLEW

◊ PUFFIN

◊ RAZORBILL

◊ SHOEBILL

◊ SPOONBILL

◊ STORK

◊ SWORD-BILLED HUMMING-BIRD

◊ WOOD-PECKER

```
S U S Y S G G S A R C M A E S
S S H T S U A S H E L D U C K
Z A O X N S H E K I R H S S N
S R E U I A S S O R S U H I D
K H B S P T M D B N N O R S X
R H I H E E O S O B R E T T S
E B L K W O S W I E S A K A A
T B L B R E C R L S R S R R N
A S E N G A D A T L K I A F D
W W P R P S R H I V R I L I E
R S B A G K W N A S A S N N R
A O M R R N G I A T L O U C L
E N D N E R U Z F R Y R S H I
H A E T P S O S C T K A E W N
S S W O L L A W S L S A S V G
```

◊ SANDERLING   ◊ SHRIKE   ◊ STAR FINCH

◊ SERIN   ◊ SISKIN   ◊ STARLING

◊ SHAG   ◊ SKYLARK   ◊ STORK

◊ SHEARWATER   ◊ SMEW   ◊ SUN LARK

◊ SHELDUCK   ◊ SNIPE   ◊ SUNBIRD

◊ SHIKRA   ◊ SNOWCAP   ◊ SUNGREBE

◊ SHOEBILL   ◊ SORA   ◊ SWALLOW

◊ SHORELARK   ◊ SPARROW   ◊ SWIFT

Bird Profile: Eurasian Nuthatch

```
Y D E T T O P S T C E S N I Y
D S E C I V E R C C S S S P A
O P E R S S O R C A N E R Z W
B O C I I N E A J N Q A E U S
L I N D M U A E E E H T P D W
U N A E I T C D R S J O N A S
E T R R L H C G T T A A L U J
I E T I A A E E V H L E N E N
S D N S R T S W K D R U R Z A
H D E E F C S A O Q S O W A I
S A Q D R H J O H U D M A P S
O B S I Z E W P A L E R U T A
N B W H I S T L E D H A R D R
G E W I N S I D E R I V E D U
C R E L A M E F E R U T A M E
```

Latin Name: *Sitta europaea*

Family: *Sittidae*

Description: The Eurasian nuthatch male has a blueish upper body with a black eye-stripe, white throat, and peach underside. The female is generally similar though paler in appearance and both have long pointed bills.

Nuthatches feed on insects such as caterpillars as well as seeds and nuts, and can be spotted descending trees head first. Their name is derived from the way they wedge nuts into crevices before smashing them with their hard bills to access the food inside.

Sounds: Repeated loud, sharp *dwip* and whistled *pee-pee-pee* song.

Distribution and habitat: The Eurasian nuthatch can be found across more temperate areas of Eurasia from the United Kingdom to Japan and often inhabits mature woodlands.

Fun Fact: It has been nicknamed the "mud dabber" due to its unusual habit of plastering mud around the entrance hole to its nest, until it is the desired size.

```
W R Z A E F L Y C A T C H E R
O N E K T L T E L E O U E B D
O E A P R T G U L H G H U R N
D R P P I Q I W Y Q W T I A L
C W R R E P O P Z O T B C J U
R O E O Y J D P T O T F R T B
E O T A T M I N N N A D O H N
E B A P G C M Q A N A R C G E
P M E B U L U R T S M I I I E
E A Y L G A E A A E I B A N R
R B E R I W I O M I D F S D G
W T N L M L M X W Z L F H E W
W O O D Q U A I L L S U A R O
R E H S I F G N I K X P G A C
R E I R R A H H C R E E P E R
```

◊ ANTBIRD

◊ ANTPITTA

◊ BAMBOO-
   WREN

◊ BUTTONQUAIL

◊ CRAKE

◊ CREEPER

◊ CROCIAS

◊ EAGLE-OWL

◊ EARED-
   NIGHTJAR

◊ FANTAIL

◊ FLYCATCHER

◊ GREENBUL

◊ HARRIER

◊ HONEYEATER

◊ KINGFISHER

◊ OWLET

◊ PICULET

◊ PUFFBIRD

◊ RAIL

◊ SANDPIPER

◊ SHAG

◊ TOWHEE

◊ WOOD-
   CREEPER

◊ WOOD-QUAIL

The Birds of Disney

```
K A V I N Z K A U Z D E W M L
V Y K C E B S Z H R K I M T Z
A F L E T X A A Q E L S N R Y
L R U E V Z Y H I B E Z W K M
I G A D L A X Z U D V Q A T Y
A K C V B L Z R E G W M L B U
N D I U E U I M V K C U D C M
T A S D B N I V G B F O O M T
A A B P M H L N R O D L I K J
R I P I C T I A G O Q F E X D
K N L R G W M O R M E T H A K
S C A E K A H K R E G G I R T
Y S U R M R I M T R V S E L R
M Z A B E A W L D A Y Y H K F
T D K Z A E T N I V E K E G O
```

◊ ABIGAIL   ◊ DARKWING   ◊ MCDUCK

◊ AMELIA   ◊ DINKY   ◊ ORVILLE

◊ ARCHIMEDES   ◊ DODO   ◊ RAVEN

◊ BECKY   ◊ FLIT   ◊ TRIGGER

◊ BOOMER   ◊ HAYABUSA   ◊ VALIANT

◊ BUCK   ◊ HEI-HEI   ◊ WALDO

◊ BUZZIE   ◊ IAGO   ◊ WILBUR

◊ DAISY   ◊ KEVIN   ◊ ZAZU

```
A B R O W N N O D D Y D T E N
G G P B O B O L I N K F F R K
N N V R E R R U M R G K I E L
I I J A V A S P A R R O W L I
H W E M L T Z K N E E D S B A
N D R B E A U B I D A O S R R
A E A L W H B A K I T V X A S
M R F I C C L L P E A E U W Y
B A D N N M U D M G U K A W A
A Z L G M L E E I N K I V O W
R I E L Q A J A L I C E H L G
N G I L A P A G E K S H Q L D
O K F A Y R Y L N J R O M E I
W E B E R G D E R A E I R Y R
L D B Z E S O O G A D A N A C
```

◊ ANHINGA

◊ BALD EAGLE

◊ BARN OWL

◊ BLUE JAY

◊ BOBOLINK

◊ BRAMBLING

◊ BROWN
  NODDY

◊ CANADA
  GOOSE

◊ CHUKAR

◊ DOVEKIE

◊ EARED
  GREBE

◊ FIELDFARE

◊ GREAT AUK

◊ JAVA
  SPARROW

◊ KING EIDER

◊ LIMPKIN

◊ MALLARD

◊ MURRE

◊ PALMCHAT

◊ REDWING

◊ RIDGWAY'S
  RAIL

◊ SORA

◊ VAUX'S SWIFT

◊ YELLOW
  WARBLER

The Dalliance of Eagles
by Walt Whitman

```
S P O O L V E D I V E R S E S
H I G N I L P P A R G E G T G
G N I U S R U P P E L R N N K
I I D G N I V I L G E E I S S
H O S A O M X U A V M T T K W
C N O A L K L E I O A S A I A
L S G W A L L R M E K E R R L
I S G N T N I A B Y B T Y T C
N A N N I L I A W W U C G I D
C M I R I T D A N P P A A N E
H W H E E L R S W C J T T G L
I E S S C D L A I T E N H Y F
N I U T Z A R A P O R O G O F
G J R E O D P M F I P C I Y U
L O O S I N G S A L L I T S M
```

SKIRTING the river road, (my forenoon walk, my rest,)

Skyward in air a sudden muffled sound, the dalliance of the
   eagles,

The rushing amorous contact high in space together,

The clinching interlocking claws, a living, fierce, gyrating wheel,

Four beating wings, two beaks, a swirling mass tight grappling,

In tumbling turning clustering loops, straight downward falling,

Till o'er the river pois'd, the twain yet one, a moment's lull,

A motionless still balance in the air, then parting, talons loosing,

Upward again on slow-firm pinions slanting, their separate diverse
   flight,

She hers, he his, pursuing.

```
K I N G V U L T U R E C A E X
E T I K L I A N S B F R I L H
E L G A E E K A N S A K E G A
X Q R I P A N S P C E G N A R
N I L R E M C H A S O A A E P
G L M I M O I R T S Z R T H Y
Y H S F P Y A R H A S I O S E
R T N S B C E A B E K F S I A
F A O N A L W K B D I U E F G
A W O N T K C V E I L Y A J L
L N S H E A A R K I H S E Y E
C Y P O L W O Y M G Y P A S G
O O R B E L W O N R A B G H S
N W E B U B A L D E A G L E T
M L Y Y R E I R R A H N E H I
```

◊ BALD EAGLE

◊ BARN OWL

◊ BATELEUR

◊ BESRA

◊ BLACK BAZA

◊ CARACARA

◊ FISH-EAGLE

◊ GOSHAWK

◊ GYRFALCON

◊ HARPY EAGLE

◊ HEN HARRIER

◊ HOBBY

◊ KESTREL

◊ KING VULTURE

◊ MERLIN

◊ OSPREY

◊ PYGMY OWL

◊ RED KITE

◊ SCOPS OWL

◊ SEA EAGLE

◊ SHIKRA

◊ SNAIL KITE

◊ SNAKE-EAGLE

◊ TAWNY OWL

Bird Profile: Kakapo

```
C I D E P O L E V E D I G S B
H O Y D E T C E T O R P W O N
I P V R W H I S K E R S W S A
M A R E E T D E B K P L P R I
S K C E R K V E F Y I S L E L
E A F C D I R A R Y H N I B A
L K S N T A N A F U S U G M M
F N D A W C T O D R T S H U M
G N N H Y I L O E N R A T N A
N B A C L L C H R I U G E O M
I O L O O C T K K S O O A F P
T O S W O A T T R A C T F I J
T M I R E L A N R U T C O N T
E N I F E N I D R A W R A C F
G S E C N A T S I D K N O W N
```

Latin Name: *Strigops habroptilus*

Family: *Strigopoidea*

Description: The kakapo is the largest parrot native to New Zealand and is moss-green with darker mottling and a pale, owl-like face and fine feathers that resemble whiskers.

The only known flightless parrots, kakapo are solitary and nocturnal. Their lack of flight does not stop them from getting around however, as they have developed strong legs and a jog-like gait allowing them to cover good distances.

Sounds: During "lekking", or engaging in courtship rituals, the male digs a bowl into which he makes a deep boom call, attempting to attract a mate.

Distribution and habitat: The introduction of mammalian predators saw numbers drop as low as 50 in the 1990s and they are now found only in small, protected numbers on certain islands.

Fun Fact: The plight of the kakapo was featured in the television series *Last Chance to See* during which Sirocco took a fancy to zoologist Mark Carwardine, gaining himself an international following.

```
N O M L N V E N I X E N V I A
E N E H A E P N H K E D D C N
M E S P M Y M H E M Y H K E L
S Q V M F A O S G P I V P C C
N A W H I R I O D C Y L T P E
I E M R S H R L N R L A J N W
K K M E P F E E M U O I L H P
B E M D N L M N B E B W E P M
N E R O A S M O N E N N S I Q
N V F N E M Y G R E L C T G L
J I X B E V L L R F Y N B P A
X P I R A F O E K T X A O E W
R R M W K M Y N E N H D C N M
T E M I L K M E N L K E A J E
N N N E M S T R O P S N N J N
```

◊ AIRMEN   ◊ HORSEMEN   ◊ PEAHEN

◊ AMEN   ◊ KEN   ◊ PIGPEN

◊ BULLPEN   ◊ KINSMEN   ◊ PLAYPEN

◊ CAYENNE   ◊ LAWMEN   ◊ SPORTSMEN

◊ CLERGYMEN   ◊ MADMEN   ◊ SWORDSMEN

◊ FEN   ◊ MAILMEN   ◊ THEN

◊ FROGMEN   ◊ MERMEN   ◊ TRIBESMEN

◊ GLEN   ◊ MILKMEN   ◊ WHEN

A Banditry of Tits

```
G R O U N D E B S C D V I E R
X A Z A K R E I O E S R C O E
K P A R U S C S I R I J A D P
D F L Z P H W R S O E P N E I
E N A I U W A U M I T A I L N
W F I A I V L O J S H E L D U
O G N L T T T C U I U J O I J
R W L V A E N O M W S E R R R
B O T N Q U E A K O S J A B C
W L Q A H R L L M E X I C A N
O M E I E A F B Z P O P H M A
L S L N Y R R V E L E G A N T
L J I A V E G B A F R I C A N
E C N D E P P A C K C A L B J
Y E S U O M T I T D E T F U T
```

◊ AFRICAN

◊ AZURE

◊ BLACK-
CAPPED

◊ BOREAL

◊ BRIDLED

◊ CAROLINA

◊ CINEREOUS

◊ COAL

◊ ELEGANT

◊ GREAT

◊ GROUND

◊ HIMALAYAN

◊ IRIOMOTE

◊ JUNIPER

◊ MEXICAN

◊ OAK

◊ PARUS

◊ SICHUAN

◊ SOMBRE

◊ SULTAN

◊ TUFTED
TITMOUSE

◊ VARIED

◊ WILLOW

◊ YELLOW-
BROWED

African...

```
K J T A H C E N O T S D N E K
I R O Z A Y K T S K I M M E R
B Y E Y K T C R E T R A D Y C
L S W I S S T R O Q S S R X K
A S W O R T A I L O R B I R D
C I T I O R E H P D H O B B Y
K R L I F K A R S W N A U E L
D F A I P T C H C U N A C O L
U I P K Q I S U H A R I C P I
C N N M E U P N C S T H D O B
K F Q U E M W A I R R C T O D
F O A Z A B J I I P K A H H A
G O S H A W K L S M E C M E O
V T E L W O D E R R A B U W R
B A Y I L L I B N O O P S B B
```

◊ BARRED OWLET

◊ BAZA

◊ BLACK DUCK

◊ BROADBILL

◊ CITRIL

◊ CRAKE

◊ CUCKOO

◊ DARTER

◊ FINFOOT

◊ GOSHAWK

◊ HOBBY

◊ HOOPOE

◊ JACANA

◊ MARSH-HARRIER

◊ OYSTER-CATCHER

◊ PIPIT

◊ PITTA

◊ SKIMMER

◊ SNIPE

◊ SPOONBILL

◊ STONECHAT

◊ SWIFT

◊ TAILORBIRD

◊ THRUSH

Birds Believed to be Symbols or Omens

```
E E D A K C I H C Y E T E R A
I R Y E R D R A M A G P I E I
U S L F O W C E R U T L U V F
Q N D V T S O A A G E K B V L
P V E Z K L E R N B Y D V Q A
R E S K V R O L C A R U X B M
A T A P C B O K G I R W I L I
V I A C I I K T B A A Y N U N
E R B N O B H G S C E R E E G
N U R O C C N C A I T I O B O
H E R O N I K M E O G P H I G
H A N D K Z B F R N T O P R X
F A L C O N E R J T A U O D X
B R O W B L A C K B I R D S N
Z M S H E P E L I C A N C F E
```

◊ BLACKBIRD

◊ BLUEBIRD

◊ CANARY

◊ CHICKADEE

◊ CHICKEN

◊ CRANE

◊ CROW

◊ DOVE

◊ EAGLE

◊ FALCON

◊ FLAMINGO

◊ GOOSE

◊ HERON

◊ MACAW

◊ MAGPIE

◊ MOCKING-
  BIRD

◊ PARROT

◊ PEACOCK

◊ PELICAN

◊ PHOENIX

◊ RAVEN

◊ ROBIN

◊ STORK

◊ VULTURE

```
C S E K W I A T N X D H R R I
N P Z N B R O S I I S I Y J A
N L Z E I X C L Q L G W M M N
I I M W G T E Q B G R U I C P
N A A I B F R A F A E L H S J
U G Z T I O S E I W I R C S H
M I R G R V A W B I B D S T U
D B M M D N O T F L I T O R E
Z A H C I O Y W G B A U T H L
H Z T L D A Y E E U Q U H S L
O E L Y M W S E K R D A E I I
O I D E D I C T A B I R D Z V
B G L W E G F Y K C E B O A R
U I A P I N G U B N D I D Z O
A V I I P G R L A A Y V O U B
```

◊ ABIGAIL

◊ ALBERTINE

◊ AMELIA

◊ BECKY

◊ BIG BIRD

◊ BILLINA

◊ DIABLO

◊ DICTABIRD

◊ FELIX

◊ FLIT

◊ HEDWIG

◊ HUGIN

◊ IAGO

◊ MUNIN

◊ ORVILLE

◊ PINGU

◊ QUOTH

◊ RAFAEL

◊ SERENA

◊ THE DODO

◊ TWEETY

◊ WILBUR

◊ WOODY

◊ ZAZU

Bird Profile: Northern Cardinal

```
D E L T S I H W A E F O U N D
T H G I A R T S F E M A L E I
N K N L S R S N E D R A G E S
O A I A P M A N W O R B N V T
I N M N R S R E D E E F I Y I
T R U I I X S I H V S N D L N
I E S D H M F N I C E E R N C
S T S R C F R B A S M S I I T
O S A A I E R D H E B T B A I
P A N C H A A R T S L I G T V
H E U T N N U A E C A N N R E
S L R T A B L B I R N G O E G
T O A C B L O E G E C J S C R
N I C Y I R D E N S E C A F A
L R N C C I L O H T A C Y M L
```

Latin Name: *Cardinalis cardinalis*

Family: *Cardinalis*

Description: The northern cardinal is a reasonably large songbird with a long tail and a distinctive crest. The male is a vibrant red all over while the female is pale brown with reddish tints to the wings, tail, and crest. Both have black faces with thick red-orange beaks.

An unassuming bird, the northern cardinal sits in a hunched-over position with its tail straight down. When not at bird feeders they may be difficult to spot but they are certainly easy to hear.

Sounds: Whistled *cheer-cheer-cheer* song and metallic chirps.

Distribution and habitat: The northern cardinal is found across the eastern United States as well as southern Canada. They are usually found in gardens, parks, and shrubby woodland, nesting in dense shrubs and vines.

Fun Fact: Cardinals get their name from their resemblance to the distinctive red robes worn by Roman Catholic Cardinals.

D R A C E B Y T A L S W D T Q
N C E B L A C K I N C A R S I
R S C S B A N A N A Q U I T Q
E O O T O P T A E R G L B E N
T O C O T O U C A N V H L L O
T T O N T T G G O E K G I A R
I E I J G Y Q P R U A U O K E
B V H N N J S T L E Q G V E H
N O E T P I E W Y E X K T D I
U D R G X A Z P I Z K Q J U M
S D O T L F R T N F Z C A C A
M E N G F A A N A R T E B K G
M R H W H I T E M O N J I T A
N A U G A C U A C G H D R C Y
A E H R N I K P M I L M U Z A

◊ AGAMI HERON

◊ BANANAQUIT

◊ BLACK INCA

◊ CAUCA GUAN

◊ COCOI HERON

◊ EARED DOVE

◊ GREAT POTOO

◊ HARPY EAGLE

◊ HOATZIN

◊ JABIRU

◊ KELP GOOSE

◊ LAKE DUCK

◊ LIMPKIN

◊ OILBIRD

◊ RHEA

◊ SILVER TEAL

◊ SLATY BECARD

◊ SOOTY SWIFT

◊ SUNBITTERN

◊ TOCO TOUCAN

◊ WHITE MONJITA

Word that Rhyme with DUCK

```
K C U K C U B H S U B V Z K K
C I A U P A W E S T R U C K C
U Z E P O C H W U J P U V T U
Z Y K H T V Z A C E L G H P L
S K C O L L I H K D S U A H P
T R U M U R D T O F N D K I P
A O B L C Y Z O M D D C T U U
R E A R K U G C E O U C C K N
S B G D Z C P R C H B K Y C S
T U E F R K S K C U H S U U T
R C M S G T O K C U T R Y L U
U K C U R T P U K C I P Z C C
C O C U Y O U N G B U C K N K
K G C U D U M B S T R U C K Q
S K G E M K C U R T S N O O M
```

◊ AWESTRUCK

◊ BUSHBUCK

◊ CHUCK

◊ CLUCK

◊ DUMBSTRUCK

◊ EPOCH

◊ GOOD LUCK

◊ HILLOCK

◊ MEGABUCK

◊ MOON-STRUCK

◊ MUCK

◊ PADDOCK

◊ PICKUP TRUCK

◊ PLUCK

◊ POTLUCK

◊ PUCK

◊ ROEBUCK

◊ SHUCK

◊ STAR-STRUCK

◊ SUCK

◊ THUNDER-STRUCK

◊ UNSTUCK

◊ YOUNG BUCK

◊ YUCK

```
E S L J P Z C X T S N E F C Y
L C L I Q W U C W N C X U V G
I V U J K Q R O P N E C R F W
D H G P T A R A A A K E E O S
O C A H K C E D S O R A R R T
C N E E I B N R O H T R D G W
O I S R Z A A S E H A G O O Q
R F E O I B R G E P G P N T Z
C D K N W A C R S T D S Z P Y
V L B O V I I G N I G N I S E
T O D E V L Z M A W H G V A L
L G N M T Y K A O D E G T J L
S K Y L A R K R R O O Z O I O
Y K R S B J C Y N D N V L X W
E E D A K C I H C A R J E C Q
```

◊ A FEAST FOR CROWS

◊ ALL THE BIRDS, SINGING

◊ BIRDS OF A FEATHER

◊ BLACK SWAN GREEN

◊ CHICKADEE

◊ FLAUBERT'S PARROT

◊ LONESOME DOVE

◊ ORYX AND CRAKE

◊ OWL MOON

◊ SEAGULL

◊ SILVER SPARROW

◊ SKYLARK

◊ THE CRANE'S DANCE

◊ THE CRANE WIFE

◊ THE CROCODILE BIRD

◊ THE CUCKOO'S CALLING

◊ THE GOLDFINCH

◊ THE HERON

◊ THE PIGEON

◊ THE RAVEN BOYS

◊ THE SNOW GEESE

◊ THE THORN BIRDS

◊ THE YELLOW BIRDS

◊ WIZARD OF THE CROW

Birds on the Box

```
K C U D D L A N O D X Z B M K
O X A L U K C U D T N U O C O
M A S N A C U O T S J U U K W
T L B X W U C C P G C D R C A
Y T O K O D Q I N I Y G J O L
Y W C K O C D R U S D S D T S
L E G A D M V L I F E G A S K
C E U D Y E R A X T Y I E D I
P T H R E G D O A E B C H O A
W Y U I T O L V W L N G G O T
U J E B P O I E O D I A G W P
F U Y G U R D Q U A C K E R B
U G N I P C R A Q C I O G A I
S B E B V S Q R E P P I K S O
E D R A Z Z U B Y K A E B E R
```

◊ BEAKY
BUZZARD

◊ BECCA

◊ BIG BIRD

◊ COUNT
DUCKULA

◊ DAISY DUCK

◊ DEWEY

◊ DONALD
DUCK

◊ EGGHEAD, JR.

◊ HUEY

◊ IAGO

◊ KOWALSKI

◊ LOUIE

◊ OWL

◊ PIDGEOT

◊ PINGU

◊ PRIVATE

◊ QUACKER

◊ RICO

◊ SCROOGE
MCDUCK

◊ SKIPPER

◊ TOUCAN SAM

◊ TWEETY

◊ WOODSTOCK

◊ WOODY

Birds Inside Words

```
S W A G N O S N A W S D W L N
E L G A E B L E B W C M S A M
B D N I G H T H A W K I T E F
E T U T I T S N O C C C G P B
N E G C J Z K F D E I R N K O
C H C T K Y E G D E T O I C W
E O R N Q B U C T K N W B I L
T S N L E V O E W M E A O H I
I U W T T H G A U A H V R C N
T O E I R N H I R H T E S C G
E N T U I A N N J D U I I C L
P E J K M A V H M B A F D W K
P V R O T L T E R A B W O R C
A A T I B W R E N C H H L J L
L R T X W W O R C E R A C S A
```

◊ APPE**TIT**E   ◊ **CROW**BAR   ◊ PE**TIT**

◊ AUT**HEN**TIC   ◊ DIS**ROBIN**G   ◊ **RAVEN**OUS

◊ B**EAGLE**   ◊ **DUCK**BOARD   ◊ SCARE**CROW**

◊ **BOWL**ING   ◊ **HEN**CE   ◊ **SWAN**KY

◊ **CHICK**PEA   ◊ HO**WL**   ◊ **SWAN**SONG

◊ CONS**TIT**UTE   ◊ **LARK**ING   ◊ **TIT**ANIUM

◊ CONT**RAVEN**E   ◊ MI**CROW**AVE   ◊ TOMA**HAWK**

◊ **CRANE**D   ◊ NIGHT**HAWK**   ◊ **WREN**CH

Bird Profile: Common Starling

```
R P L U M A G E U R A S I A V
E R A E P S E K A H S T E B S
S I R I D E S C E N T S X U L
O S L A S R O T A D E R P N A
L M R F N V Y M A S S I A D E
C Y A E R I A L E R D F N A V
E C S N F A M T E E L U D N E
S B S I Y F I A H G O I I C R
K I O E O S O C L R R H N E N
C L R L A N R Y G S S A G G E
O L C R G E A K R X G K L V E
L J A A P G E C E V O M I A B
F P T E I D P O E C A T T L E
M R O F R E P T N I A L P V L
R E T N I W A S S N O M M O C
```

Latin Name: *Sturnus vulgaris*

Family: *Sturnidae*

Description: A small, stocky bird with a yellow bill, the common starling can, on first sight, appear to be a plain and dark bird. However, closer inspection reveals a beautiful plumage shimmering with iridescent blues and greens.

The common starling eats a largely insectivorous diet for which it forages on the ground. They are also sometimes seen perched on top of animals, such as cattle, feeding on the parasites to be found there.

Sounds: Large flocks mean they can be rather noisy and they have a skill for mimicry that has impressed many, including Shakespeare.

Distribution and Habitat: The common starling is native to Eurasia, but has been introduced across the globe, and is found in abundance.

Fun Fact: On winter evenings starlings perform impressive aerial displays called murmurations. These huge, swarm-like flocks move in sync, swooping, contracting, and expanding as they go. It is believed that this mass movement offers protection from predators.

Residents of the Rainforest and Tropics

```
Z O E L G A E Y P R A H E I F
O T C R I M S O N T O P A Z N
P W O V X W V K A R A E L I M
A O U U J A B I R U S T O R K
R O N K C C N N E M A S D A B
R D C I T A A G D P L L N C Q
O C M N R M N V L E L O E A C
T R O G O N T U O T I R P R A
A E G F P H S L R E B I O A R
N E M I I O H T Y R D K R Q A
T P O S C A R U Q Z A E O D C
B E T H B T I R B D O E A Y A
I R M E I Z K E H M R T V Y R
R E O R R I E B U L B U L I A
D H T Y D N N I G H T H A W K
```

◊ ANTBIRD

◊ ANTSHRIKE

◊ ARACARI

◊ BROADBILL

◊ BULBUL

◊ CARACARA

◊ CRIMSON TOPAZ

◊ HARPY EAGLE

◊ HOATZIN

◊ JABIRU STORK

◊ KING VULTURE

◊ KINGFISHER

◊ LORIKEET

◊ MACAW

◊ MOTMOT

◊ NIGHTHAWK

◊ OROPENDOLA

◊ PARROT

◊ RED LORY

◊ TOUCAN

◊ TROGON

◊ TROPICBIRD

◊ TRUMPETER

◊ WOOD-CREEPER

Gruiformes

```
H E L U N I L L A G V A R O S
L N I D J W N A T I V E H E N
I A A R G U A M R A I L B B E
M C R A N E N T V N W G R E K
P I G T L E E I E J O K H R A
K R N S U T H H N R M E U G R
I O I U R C R D I C C R L N C
N L K B O E O G O C R O Y U N
F F D T T Y O J J O R A C S R
I L Z A B X M R O B W J K K O
N A W E R U D D Y C R A K E C
F G Y R L I A T F F U L F O W
O N B G C X K P Z W B G O U O
O E S W A M P H E N N T A P O
T B J N R E T T I B N U S K O
```

- ◊ BENGAL FLORICAN
- ◊ BROLGA
- ◊ COOT
- ◊ CORN CRAKE
- ◊ FINFOOT
- ◊ FLUFFTAIL
- ◊ GALLINULE
- ◊ GREAT BUSTARD
- ◊ GUAM RAIL
- ◊ JUNIN CRAKE
- ◊ KAGU
- ◊ KING RAIL
- ◊ LIMPKIN
- ◊ MOORHEN
- ◊ NATIVEHEN
- ◊ RUDDY CRAKE
- ◊ SORA
- ◊ SUNBITTERN
- ◊ SUNGREBE
- ◊ SWAMPHEN
- ◊ WATERCOCK
- ◊ WATERHEN
- ◊ WEKA
- ◊ WOODHEN

```
I U A Y W L W O F A E N I U G
E W F E E T F T N A S A E H P
C L Q I G K P I Z E F C L W H
B I T E G D R I W E K M N Q F
W L T T M A I U G D U C K X R
O E I S A S N R T E A G I G A
M R N W E W W D T R O A V H N
M E A R B M Q A E R G N U P C
A K M A U S O O N R A F F S O
T C O S Y S S D R E G P D R L
N O U U Q T E P O E H C H S I
A C L U R U J E H K R E N Y N
B P A I Q Q A G G A A O P Y C
T I C U L D C B E R O R K N A
L H P E A F O W L D E S O O G
```

◊ BANTAM   ◊ GOOSE   ◊ QUAIL

◊ CHICKEN   ◊ GUINEAFOWL   ◊ RHEA

◊ COCKEREL   ◊ LEGHORN   ◊ SNOOD

◊ DOMESTIC   ◊ OSTRICH   ◊ SQUAB

◊ DRAKE   ◊ PARTRIDGE   ◊ SWAN

◊ DUCK   ◊ PEAFOWL   ◊ TINAMOU

◊ FRANCOLIN ◊ PHEASANT   ◊ TURKEY

◊ GANDER   ◊ PIGEON   ◊ WATTLE

The Hawk by W.B. Yeats

```
E R A B Y C A G E D A E J T D
V N E W D L U O H S O I I U U
A D R D R Z J E A S X W R M M
N C D A R I V M W N P W N B B
K L F N G A S B K D O I X L F
T A S U E E L T R L L H T I O
D P X L Z I D L L O L I W N U
A P C W G T R E I Z K L M G N
A E E I D N Y F A W A E A T D
L D Y L N R I P R E T E N C E
I Z E D I A R N E R O F E B D
G T S I M E Z O E Z W H A T U
H S C U L L I O N V C O O K O
T P R O U D G N I R E V O H L
S D N W O R G D E D O O H D C
```

'Call down the hawk from the air;
Let him be hooded or caged
Till the yellow eye has grown mild,
For larder and spit are bare,
The old cook enraged,
The scullion gone wild.'

'I will not be clapped in a hood,
Nor a cage, nor alight upon wrist,
Now I have learnt to be proud
Hovering over the wood
In the broken mist
Or tumbling cloud.'

'What tumbling cloud did you cleave,
Yellow-eyed hawk of the mind,
Last evening? that I, who had sat
Dumbfounded before a knave,
Should give to my friend
A pretence of wit.'

```
D D T R E N I M N O M M O C D
R R R R S C Y T H E B I L L R
I I E C E I M N A R A O I X I
B B E H S T G S E H N H A E B
W B C A E A A N R G T O T N T
O U R T D O I E A L W R E O A
C R E M O M H G Y V R N N P C
A C E Q L D K R A E E E I S I
N S P L C C E A D I N R P F S
A T E I N B G S I R U O S T S
S B R A I T O S T P I T H R S
T S R R C Q X W O E A B V O N
E H D B O W E R B I R D G B L
R B R I S T L E B I R D M I S
O C L V S P I N E B I L L N F
```

◊ ANTWREN

◊ BELL MINER

◊ BOWERBIRD

◊ BRISTLEBIRD

◊ CANASTERO

◊ CATBIRD

◊ CHAT

◊ CINCLODES

◊ COMMON MINER

◊ COWBIRD

◊ FIGBIRD

◊ GRASSWREN

◊ HONEYEATER

◊ HORNERO

◊ LYREBIRD

◊ RAYADITO

◊ ROBIN

◊ SCRUBBIRD

◊ SCYTHEBILL

◊ SPINEBILL

◊ SPINETAIL

◊ TREE-CREEPER

◊ TUI

◊ XENOPS

Bird Profile:
Emperor Penguin

```
R M G B A V O U T W A R D T N
E R N L N A L A R G E S T H I
B A I A T G N I L D D U H T U
M W R C A R C O U N T E D R G
U A P K R A V D G R O U P O N
N J S S C N A Y A T C S I N E
S S F S T T S Z H E R P W D P
E P F N I S T E M E H A S N Y
I T O U C V R P H A T C G A F
N U D T A S E T F E T E N L I
O R R F T R A N R R F E I K T
L N I I O E T I H W O I W L N
O S B R F D D N U O F Z L A E
C H S R A H T S E H C N E F D
R O T A T E G E O R G I A N I
```

Latin Name: *Aptenodytes forsteri*

Family: *Spheniscidae*

Description: The largest of the penguins, this streamlined bird is well-adapted for life in the water. It has black feathers on its head, neck, flipper-like wings, and back. It has a white front that is yellower at the chest and orange/pink under the chin and a long, black bill.

Emperor penguins rely on the group to survive their harsh environment. Huddling together in massive packs, they rotate inward and outward taking turns to warm up and warm the others.

Sounds: The emperor penguin makes a vast number of calls to identify its mate and offspring among the masses.

Distribution and Habitat: Mostly found in the vast, frozen expanses of Antarctica, some vagrants have been found further north in areas such as the Falkland Islands and South Georgia.

Fun Fact: So vast are the massive emperor penguin colonies that they have been spotted and counted from space!

```
R K L L L I B T O R R A P R N
R E H S A R H T O D L W E U A
L L I B X A W M R S O G W H H
B U N T I N G I E R R N O W C
R E L B B A B E R Q I I O R N
H S U R H T D A H G O L D E I
L C J G A E P S H F L R L L F
A C O C A S Y T K A E A A B D
N P M T D G I W W Y X T R R L
I O E K K N E S A C L S K A O
D R W A G T A I L X Z A W W G
R E G A N A T M K D W D R I D
A F L Y C A T C H E R I S K V
C E E K I D U N N O C K N H E
S H R E T A E Y E N O H E G K
```

◊ BABBLER   ◊ NIGHTINGALE   ◊ TANAGER

◊ BUNTING   ◊ ORIOLE   ◊ THRASHER

◊ CARDINAL   ◊ PARROTBILL   ◊ THRUSH

◊ CATBIRD   ◊ SEEDEATER   ◊ WAGTAIL

◊ DUNNOCK   ◊ SKYLARK   ◊ WARBLER

◊ FLYCATCHER   ◊ SPARROW   ◊ WAXBILL

◊ GOLDFINCH   ◊ STARLING   ◊ WAXWING

◊ HONEYEATER   ◊ SWALLOW   ◊ WOODLARK

```
E E K I L N A M K R O W C R F
M I N I B I K E K I L H C U S
D E E K I L E V A W I R I K E
E E K U J E L L Y L I K E I K
O K O I C E G O D L I K E S R
I I I O L G V L A D Y L I K E
G B F L F A I M I K E O U K T
H R I I A K K P M E S N Y D U
P O K E E N E O Q K L D K O R
S T E V H K U G O I L I H G N
Y O C C I S P Z K L S K R L P
C M I L X R H E O E P E D I I
H E S W E K I A Y F I R Y K K
R I O V E R S T R I K E J E E
D R E A M L I K E L E L I K E
```

◊ CHILDLIKE   ◊ LADYLIKE   ◊ REICH

◊ DISLIKE   ◊ LIFELIKE   ◊ SPIKE

◊ DOGLIKE   ◊ LOOKALIKE   ◊ SUCHLIKE

◊ DREAMLIKE   ◊ MIKE   ◊ TURNPIKE

◊ DYKE   ◊ MINIBIKE   ◊ UNALIKE

◊ GODLIKE   ◊ MOTORBIKE   ◊ UNLIKE

◊ JELLYLIKE   ◊ OVERSTRIKE   ◊ WAVELIKE

◊ KLONDIKE   ◊ PSYCH   ◊ WORKMAN-
                                                LIKE

```
C T O O F N E K C I H C F E R
H D S E L G A E O P S H A P S
I R E W O R C U E W O R E H F
C A J S B T P N K U Q L E L D
K K J Y E R G S S R I A A V S
S E R S M U E E Q C R M K G K
A D I N I L M I A W I Y N Q W
S H O N O A V N A N S I R W A
D I S I R D W T G F L G O E H
O R R T Q J E O U S L L O I Y
V O I S C R S R O N U H S R A
E N Z B W K M G E A G C T D J
S T A R L I N G S W A N E O E
S S O R T A B L A S E I R W L
B L A C K H A W K E S F E L I
```

◊ AN ALBATROSS

◊ ANDREW BIRD

◊ ATOMIC ROOSTER

◊ BLACKHAWK BAND

◊ CHICKEN-FOOT

◊ DIXIE CHICKS

◊ FINCH

◊ FLOCK OF SEAGULLS

◊ JAYHAWKS

◊ NICK DRAKE

◊ ORIOLES

◊ PELICAN

◊ SHEARWATER

◊ SHERYL CROW

◊ THE BYRDS

◊ THE DOVES

◊ THE EAGLES

◊ THE FLAMINGOS

◊ THE GOSLINGS

◊ THE HOUSE-MARTINS

◊ THE PENGUINS

◊ THE STARLINGS

◊ WEIRD OWL

◊ YELLOW SWANS

Famous Birdwatchers

```
O D J K L E H N E R T M V B P
F H R E K A E S T N E R D N R
U K W O I E O R N A D N K O I
B I P V F W U O S S O R F R N
S D W U H F Q C A R T E R T C
O D D I E P I T M A N N A S E
Y M J N N S Q L E Z E E N O P
R B W V U T D E C V J W Z R H
O E A K T L E S A L F M E N I
C E T I O K R R D X N A N U L
K Q S S L E C E L R B N U E L
H R Z C A E P W D E A B W B I
E F A V G M Y P I E U W E K P
G U L L I C K R E C C A D L Z
T D S F C P S Y K L N Q A E S
```

◊ BAILEY

◊ BEAN

◊ BEIRS

◊ BUCK

◊ CARTER

◊ CEDERLUND

◊ CLARK

◊ CLIFFORD

◊ CRAVEN

◊ EDWARDS

◊ FRANZEN

◊ GULLICK

◊ KAESTNER

◊ KOEPPEL

◊ LEHNERT

◊ LEWIS

◊ MASTER

◊ NEWMAN

◊ ODDIE

◊ PITMAN

◊ PRINCE
  PHILLIP

◊ ROSSOUW

◊ ROSTRON

◊ WINTER

```
E N C E R E R L B S P O E R C
L A C R O S S B I L L T Y E A
T R I M P Y A C E N N E Y A C
T A C A C T U S K R A L C G S
A C H A T S H R I K E O O D E
C A N E G C B A C U U C C N S
A R C H C M R A K U H C R R T
N A N U O C A A C H G U O H C
A C H C C V I P N G I D Z N A
R C K E K K C T C E N I E E E
Y R T N A R O M R O C C T K G
T O K J T T K O C I U Q A C K
E W I R I C U A S T L R Z I P
E E A A E O C D I I C Y S H O
C A T A L C P A G C R A B C C
```

◊ CACTUS WREN

◊ CANARY

◊ CARACARA

◊ CATTLE TYRANT

◊ CAYENNE JAY

◊ CHATSHRIKE

◊ CHICKEN

◊ CHOUGH

◊ CHUKAR

◊ CITRIL FINCH

◊ CLARK'S GREBE

◊ COCKATIEL

◊ COLETO

◊ COMB DUCK

◊ CONDOR

◊ CORMORANT

◊ CRAB PLOVER

◊ CRAKE

◊ CRANE

◊ CROSSBILL

◊ CROW

◊ CROZET SHAG

◊ CUCKOO

◊ CUTIA

```
A A W Z L D E C K K A D H L B
G G U O A I P P E A G J O E U
N N X U L E A S Z E N J O K S
A R H M T L U U S B I D M I T
V I O R J O A E Q S T A Z R A
U C E C R A E W I O O C T H R
L L N G K D Y L S R C N E S D
Q I N U E T N M A G P I E O B
D E A A T W H E O C Z S K O U
R X T T B H K R O A S K I K N
C E C R N C A U U P U Y R C T
R C I R U A A T J S I X O U I
A E U D I A F V C R H T L C N
N U H C N I F F A H C B T U G
E A R E D P H E A S A N T A Z
```

◊ BUNTING

◊ BUSTARD

◊ CHAFFINCH

◊ COTINGA

◊ COUA

◊ CRANE

◊ CUCKOO-
  SHRIKE

◊ DACNIS

◊ DUCK

◊ EARED-
  PHEASANT

◊ FANTAIL

◊ GROSBEAK

◊ GROUSE

◊ JAY

◊ LORIKEET

◊ MAGPIE

◊ NUTHATCH

◊ PETREL

◊ PITTA

◊ QUAIL

◊ ROCK-
  THRUSH

◊ SEEDEATER

◊ SWALLOW

◊ VANGA

Bird Profile: Dalmatian Pelican

```
E U R A S I A M T A O R H T N
P U L S A T E S C R U F F Y Z
E D C N L M P M A N D I B L E
V Y B T B E C E N T R A L F N
A H L E C I S W D E N E P O A
P I R I D A O S V E L O R U I
O S E S M R R G N I T A M N T
R S E R C A A S Y A L P H D A
A P X E K Q F G O U N T C N M
T A T V R U P E G R S E K A L
I L A I A I W E T L A N D C A
O E N R B E A K R Z E N T I D
N R T C A T C H I N G D G L J
P F E A T H E R S K T I M E S
P O U C H R E T T U L F D P O
```

Latin Name: *Pelecanus crispus*

Family: *Pelecanidae*

Description: The largest <u>member</u> of the pelican <u>family</u>, the <u>Dalmatian</u> pelican is often described <u>less</u> than kindly as <u>scruffy</u> looking, with the dirty white <u>feathers</u> at its <u>crown</u> contributing to its <u>bedraggled</u> appearance. The large <u>beak</u> pouch and lower <u>mandible</u> are bright <u>orange</u> in breeding season and <u>paler</u> yellow at other <u>times</u>. It is one of the largest <u>extant</u> flying bird <u>species</u>.

Sounds: Like other <u>pelican</u> family members, the Dalmatian pelican is a <u>quiet</u> bird but may <u>bark</u> and <u>hiss</u> during <u>mating</u> season.

Distribution and Habitat: The Dalmatian pelican is <u>found</u> in <u>lakes</u>, <u>rivers</u>, and <u>wetland</u> habitats across much of <u>central</u> <u>Eurasia</u>.

Fun Fact: The beak <u>pouch</u> of the pelican, called the <u>gular</u> pouch, is not only used for <u>catching</u> food, it also <u>plays</u> an important <u>role</u> in cooling the bird. The bill is <u>opened</u> as the <u>throat</u> and pouch <u>pulsate</u> in a "gular <u>flutter</u>", encouraging cooling through <u>evaporation</u>.

```
U B R E T O C S G A N M G S E
C S L S O X H C R A K E N N T
G J C I P X O A J R Z X I E L
O R E T A E E E B E E B W T I
S I U H O T I P T K O D W E T
H A P A A M N N S C Z D A B S
A H I E G N O A A E C L S H B
W B H B G R T J F P M F B U A
K W B H E U J B X Y Z U P C C
N Y A H M T A L I R Q W N W X
O E Z J R X L N G R N I W I H
C H A A P H O E B E D J B Q A
L B I T T E R N T B I S H O P
A B H O N E Y B U Z Z A R D H
F D U C N E R W S S A R G W G
```

◊ ANTBIRD

◊ BAZA

◊ BEE-EATER

◊ BERRY-
   PECKER

◊ BISHOP

◊ BITTERN

◊ CRAKE

◊ FALCON

◊ FANTAIL

◊ GOSHAWK

◊ GRASSWREN

◊ GUAN

◊ HERON

◊ HONEY-
   BUZZARD

◊ INCA

◊ JACOBIN

◊ LORY

◊ MUNIA

◊ PHOEBE

◊ PITOHUI

◊ SAW-WING

◊ SCOTER

◊ STILT

◊ WHEATEAR

```
Z T D U B A R R A B A N D N J
U G S I W E L T T O B B A O S
V S B O L G V F H V S P C X N
E B K R A A O A L G W G S I N
I R L G E O R R R O I U X D I
Q O E J O N S S O N W N W A U
G W E Y Y K D D E Y P F K U Q
A N Q W B A T E R N E U V D N
L E I H N H V E R L B Y R U B
E M K H O U T T L S U O T B R
R S N R C A S A A M S K D O O
A M P K L A C D K E V B F N O
V E H S M I T H I X G N I T K
A S O R M A U D E B E R T P S
M U L L A R N E Y A B C Q V D
```

◊ ABBOTT

◊ AUDEBERT

◊ AUDUBON

◊ BARRABAND

◊ BRENDERS

◊ BROOKS

◊ BROWNE

◊ CHING

◊ DIXON

◊ GAGE

◊ JONSSON

◊ KNIGHT

◊ LARSEN

◊ LEWIS

◊ MICALLEF

◊ MULLARNEY

◊ QUINN

◊ ROSE

◊ SLATER

◊ SMITH

◊ TINGXI

◊ VARELA

◊ WOLF

◊ WOOD-
THORPE

Birds with Seven-letter Names – Part Two

```
H C R A N O M Y M N C R E C G
M Q C D J G C B K G F M K N X
M Q L P U O M A N I T B I H Z
M O U R N E R I R K N U X O R
E G R A C K L E S U G G E R E
C B C N N S H M S N O R L N L
N A H R O J G L E R O T E E T
A B I G E C T P S O U W B R T
L B C B E E A H S Q K O C O A
O L K U V L P T O C E Y C A T
T E E I L H E E B A S E G U P
R R N E S R F R R I T B N W J
O I R J A C K D A W R Z H X Q
M O S A R C E G A U E D I Z P
C O W B I R D U Q E L F O N Q
```

◊ BABBLER

◊ CATBIRD

◊ CHICKEN

◊ CORELLA

◊ COURSER

◊ COWBIRD

◊ CREEPER

◊ GOSLING

◊ GRACKLE

◊ HOATZIN

◊ HORNERO

◊ JACKDAW

◊ KESTREL

◊ KINGLET

◊ MINIVET

◊ MONARCH

◊ MOURNER

◊ ORTOLAN

◊ PENGUIN

◊ ROOSTER

◊ SNOWCAP

◊ TATTLER

◊ TINAMOU

◊ TOURACO

Goshawks

```
R S S D E K C A B Y T A L S G
W A A A W A S U L A W E S I N
D C B M D O R I A S U N W D I
E D I A T N S K E A E U E T T
I E M L G S U P I W B R D C N
L L I J I E I S B H J E N R A
L I T T N E Z R R Q S A P E H
E A A U D R I N H E C C A S C
B T T Y P T E H A C S E L T N
E T O F A L E H U C L S P E R
T O R I I N A L T B I E E D E
I P N M S J O R U R Y R C L T
H S A T P M I A E O O E F D S
W A S M E Y E R S W A N R A A
S E D A R K C H A N T I N G E
```

◊ AFRICAN   ◊ GABAR   ◊ NORTHERN

◊ BROWN   ◊ GREY   ◊ PIED

◊ CHRISTMAS   ◊ HENST'S   ◊ RED

◊ CRESTED   ◊ IMITATOR   ◊ SHIKRA

◊ DARK   ◊ LESSER   ◊ SLATY-
  CHANTING   SUNDAS   BACKED

◊ DORIA'S   ◊ MEYER'S   ◊ SPOT-TAILED

◊ EASTERN   ◊ MOLUCCAN   ◊ SULAWESI
  CHANTING
                  ◊ NEW BRITAIN   ◊ WHITE-
◊ FIJI   BELLIED

Birds with Six-letter names

```
M U D Q Y K N I L N U D L O T
F P M T O C K T I W E E P W D
A U K L E T D T R E O G P T M
T D R A V O C E T T Q F H L H
T E L T M N O E G I P T L L Q
O X L T D B N J W C C D I E U
U Z F G M R D M Y O G N U O E
C T U R A C O B U D N S G P L
A D A R T E R C R E N N A L E
N O R I G M A Z T O O E O Z A
A V A W E L R U C R L E Q K B
S N W Q E L C X D O R G F C L
Y E M A G P I E I I R Z A C S
T H R U S H Y R E Y H B J H J
B W F A X N O W A Y R A N A C
```

◊ AUKLET ◊ DRONGO ◊ ORIGMA

◊ AVOCET ◊ DUNLIN ◊ ORIOLE

◊ BROLGA ◊ EAGLET ◊ PEEWIT

◊ CANARY ◊ ELF OWL ◊ PIGEON

◊ CONDOR ◊ LANNER ◊ QUELEA

◊ COUCAL ◊ LINNET ◊ THRUSH

◊ CURLEW ◊ LOERIE ◊ TOUCAN

◊ DARTER ◊ MAGPIE ◊ TURACO

Bird Profile: Mute Swan

```
E Z Z G N I T N U R G K P U W
D H O M E H Q T P S G R O U P
R R Y L G U N M N S I N G L E
O N Y K I A B N A M E J J A I
W R N E G L O F A N L C M A N
X O T E A M D R K G Y E I G T
B B L C U L I A N G R S E G R
H E K T E L E I N I A T R R O
G N E K Y B S E C R I S U E D
U X A K Q S T A U H K A T S U
A M W W I M S E W F E L A S C
L Y E H S W W U S E T A M I E
Z L H M O N O G A M O U S V D
L R S D O O R B O S D K C E N
Y L I S A E G D U C K L I N G
```

Latin Name: *Cygnus olor*

Family: *Anatidae*

Description: A large white waterfowl, easily identifiable by its orange-red bill, black face, and S-shaped neck. The mature bird has a black knob above its beak. The mute swan is monogamous, territorial, and aggressive, so smaller bodies of water will typically be home to just a single pair.

Sounds: As indicated by the word "mute" in their name, they are a quiet species though they do make some grunting, snorting, and hissing sounds as well as greeting mates and their broods.

Distribution and Habitat: Primarily found across Eurasia, they have been introduced in North America.

Fun Fact: *The Ugly Duckling* tells of a cygnet—baby swan—born into a group of ducklings and considered hideously ugly by comparison. Ill-treated by many, he has the last laugh when he grows into a beautiful and elegant mute swan.

```
A N S U E R O S I R E P K Y S
E A G A R R U L U S G C A U B
N T S R O W E C I E Y J O O A
F T I O Y I O A E A O E F R G
E I K F C R G R N T C L A E A
P C N F V G N O C A O M O K R
I O E U N E L I L H O J R C F
A R S A V Y L O U C A U U A I
P D B A C E I K O C R Y H R C
I N R A R V U L K O U G M C U
A E T U F T E D C C U W O T N
C D Y B G H A I A O B G J U E
L I V W P W S T H F X F S N H
H S N A W S A C M A G P I E V
P E R M A N E I P E E R T M G
```

◊ APHELOCOMA

◊ BANGGAI

◊ BORNEAN TREEPIE

◊ CAYENNE JAY

◊ CHOUGH

◊ COLOEUS

◊ CORVUS

◊ CYANOLYCA

◊ DENDROCITTA

◊ FOREST RAVEN

◊ GARRULUS

◊ IBERIAN MAGPIE

◊ JACKDAW

◊ NUCIFRAGA

◊ NUTCRACKER

◊ PERISOREUS

◊ PIAPIAC

◊ RELICT

◊ ROOK

◊ SOMALI CROW

◊ TUFTED

◊ UROCISSA

◊ VIOLACEOUS

◊ YUCATAN

```
S J Y F Q I C A L M B Y O J S
D O O W F L Y E C L D L L Y U
S G N I W T A H O O I O O D M
Q H D T D V A S S V U U N V M
X E E M E R S T E O G D E I E
Y A R S M O I E D I R P L L R
L R D I M O Q N D L O R Y M S
U D N S T Y R D K L V B O V T
R G A L S N E N B S E U E W A
T N N Y E O W E I U R I K A E
B I E O L M O I S N I Q F T R
H N E F L R B R Z W G L O H T
G E R A E A T F T S E N D G E
I V G I W H E R E L L E T I R
H E Y R D T N E L I S Y T N Z
```

He. Where thou dwellest, in
   what grove,
Tell me Fair One, tell me Love;
Where thou thy charming nest
   dost build,
O thou pride of every field!

She. Yonder stands a lonely
   tree,
There I live and mourn for thee;
Morning drinks my silent tear,
And evening winds my sorrow
   bear.
He. O thou summer's harmony,
I have liv'd and mourn'd for
   thee;
Each day I mourn along the
   wood,

And night hath heard my
   sorrows loud.
She. Dost thou truly long for
   me?
And am I thus sweet to thee?
Sorrow now is at an end,
O my Lover and my Friend!

He. Come, on wings of joy we'll
   fly
To where my bower hangs
   on high;
Come, and make thy calm
   retreat
Among green leaves and
   blossoms sweet.

```
R E S A V N I B O R A K R E R
T F N R A N E S R E Z C A R A
N C O E I R A R G N E O I E G
K S I L V F E N R N N R N G N
Y E E L J A L E B U T Q B E I
R K R O E R R E D R D I O N T
O R O R O R A R M D O D W T S
O D A Y C I R E E A U R S N E
S A A D T A P V F O N U H G R
T L I H D S E I N R E A N R L
E R E J H E U R Z G N I R O M
R C A O R Z S R Y M W F T O D
L H T A A O R O K D F P B K P
S U O F U R H X E U A T F D U
O R E A B S S R R T D E T A R
```

◊ RADDE'S
ACCENTOR

◊ RADJAH
SHELDUCK

◊ RAINBOW
PITTA

◊ RAVEN

◊ REDWING

◊ REED
BUNTING

◊ REGENT
PARROT

◊ RELICT GULL

◊ RESTINGA
ANTWREN

◊ RIFLEMAN

◊ RING OUZEL

◊ RIVER TERN

```
N O I N U E R F A O P U N A Z
Y S A G A L A M Y Y N A O B G
X D O W J L S C I A I N M B R
X E L T B A N Z I L A Q A B G
M P I I C Y V S A C F L U D I
T A V R B O A R I P D F C E A
C N E C T R T R U O F E Y K N
R D J E U S F E G N Q M S C T
E E Z E U A J Q E X H O S E D
S R R A M N I C J X R T O N E
T C J N A W K N E E Q O L W L
E H U E I E H A D A D A G A T
D Z D E D C U I I M W S Q R T
Z N H R N R E H T R O N O T A
A P X G S O U T H E R N R S W
```

◊ AFRICAN

◊ ANDEAN

◊ AUSTRALIAN

◊ BALD

◊ BUFF-NECKED

◊ CRESTED

◊ EURASIAN

◊ GIANT

◊ GLOSSY

◊ GREEN

◊ HADADA

◊ MALAGASY

◊ NORTHERN

◊ OLIVE

◊ PUNA

◊ RED-NAPED

◊ REUNION

◊ ROYAL

◊ SACRED

◊ SAO TOME

◊ SOUTHERN

◊ STRAW-
  NECKED

◊ WATTLED

◊ WHITE

```
Y B B N E M S M O U N T E O S
R I R I M G G I L E T H L E R
A R F C R C O F C I A S T M A
I D J O P D V C L T S C T A L
N F X M M B G O S E Z U O G U
C E L P T O W U N C E O B N C
O E E A Q H G R I T U C R I O
A D N S S X A E J D M H E F N
T E P S T H P R P Q E E T I I
R R S E V O L G A V G C A E B
I F K W C P V I M O R K W R Z
P Y I S E Y Q F G O C L H D K
O N O T E B O O K H K I P M P
D A R E M A C L O O T S J E U
K C A P K C A B B O O T S O N
```

◊ BACKPACK
◊ BINOCULARS
◊ BIRD FEEDER
◊ BIRD GUIDE
◊ BOOTS
◊ CAMERA
◊ CHECKLIST
◊ COMPASS

◊ FLASHLIGHT
◊ FLEECE
◊ GILET
◊ GLOVES
◊ HARNESS
◊ HATS
◊ MAGNIFIER
◊ MAP

◊ MOUNT
◊ NOTEBOOK
◊ PEN
◊ RAINCOAT
◊ SCOPE
◊ STOOL
◊ TRIPOD
◊ WATER
  BOTTLE

Bird Profile: Great Spotted Kiwi

D	N	A	L	B	U	R	C	S	E	G	A	R	O	F
N	W	E	U	Q	I	N	U	H	E	A	V	I	L	Y
U	H	T	S	E	G	R	A	L	E	T	I	H	W	T
O	I	D	R	O	O	P	F	E	A	T	H	E	R	S
S	S	U	L	W	Z	R	B	A	N	D	E	D	E	F
B	T	E	O	A	E	Y	E	S	I	G	H	T	N	N
H	L	T	S	W	N	C	O	M	M	O	N	U	D	O
O	I	P	O	T	O	R	C	R	E	V	I	C	E	S
L	N	L	A	L	S	K	U	L	H	T	Q	G	M	T
L	G	M	T	L	S	E	I	T	L	M	R	N	I	R
O	R	S	H	A	E	P	R	W	C	E	A	O	C	I
W	E	O	G	C	C	A	Y	O	I	O	M	L	H	L
S	A	U	I	G	N	I	L	F	F	U	N	S	E	S
U	T	T	N	P	U	R	S	U	I	T	I	P	S	S
E	M	H	E	A	D	S	Z	D	E	L	T	T	O	M

Latin Name: *Apteryx haastii*

Family: *Apterygidae*

Description: Among the largest and tallest of kiwis, the great spotted kiwi has light ashy-brown feathers that are banded or mottled with white, a small head and eyes, short legs, and a long, slim, pale bill.

It is flightless and nocturnal, resting in hollows, burrows, and rock crevices during the day. It forages during the night, tapping and snuffling along in its pursuit of invertebrates to eat.

Sounds: Males make a high-pitched repeated whistling sound; the female's call is a lower whistle and pairs are known to duet.

Distribution and habitat: They are endemic to New Zealand's South Island where they are found in scrubland, grassland, and forests.

Fun Fact: In common with other kiwis, but unique amongst other birds, they have nostrils on the tips of their beaks—they rely heavily on their sense of smell as their eyesight is poor.

```
E  B  W  E  S  O  O  G  Y  E  R  G  C  F  E
I  R  E  L  G  A  E  W  D  E  U  S  H  N  I
Z  C  A  G  E  D  O  I  K  K  N  U  I  D  D
W  I  N  T  E  R  S  C  N  O  A  F  C  S  R
W  I  C  E  R  C  E  L  E  R  R  E  K  M  I
A  R  Q  A  O  P  R  G  I  U  T  Y  E  S  B
L  N  P  Z  D  F  I  B  S  T  L  B  N  T  D
B  S  F  O  A  P  W  X  E  A  T  H  K  R  B
A  K  O  O  K  A  B  U  R  R  A  L  I  A  L
T  W  L  X  O  L  O  K  Z  F  W  B  E  N  U
R  Q  I  P  K  L  T  X  V  T  K  N  P  G  E
O  J  B  F  A  Q  I  H  X  C  B  L  J  E  B
S  Q  R  N  Q  G  F  L  A  M  I  N  G  O  I
S  E  Y  O  J  V  U  L  T  U  R  E  S  Q  R
E  U  S  D  R  I  B  W  O  N  S  L  H  Q  D
```

◊ ALBATROSS

◊ ALOUETTE

◊ BIRD ON THE WIRE

◊ BIRD SET FREE

◊ BLACKBIRD

◊ BLUEBIRD

◊ CAGED BIRD

◊ DISCO DUCK

◊ FLAMINGO

◊ FLY LIKE AN EAGLE

◊ GREY GOOSE

◊ KOOKABURRA

◊ SALLY'S PIGEONS

◊ SKYLARK

◊ SNOWBIRD

◊ SPARROW

◊ STRANGE BIRDS

◊ SURFIN' BIRD

◊ THE BIRDIE SONG

◊ THE CHICKEN SONG

◊ THE WOOD-PECKER SONG

◊ THREE LITTLE BIRDS

◊ VULTURES

◊ WINTER BIRD

```
L S L X A T E N O D R O G N S
P R G E N N S T U E H E L M N
S Q H A P H M Y T P U O A A E
E E R O A P Y R R E T S L R T
N G K E D G E H P P V U V Z S
A N T O I E H O E P P O G L I
M O H A T Y S T K E T U L U N
F S N U A S I H T R O L M F G
U P O D W H Q E K B L C L F E
A M S U W X R E M E V L X O R
K O S B H S M A H R E S G A D
Q H N O O U S C U G G M C R B
B T E N H C I R N Y E L B I S
Z E V Z I M B A N E I R B O O
G Z S K T S I U Q L H A S P V
```

◊ AHLQUIST	◊ KOEPPEL	◊ RHODES
◊ ANGELL	◊ LOVETTE	◊ SIBLEY
◊ AUDUBON	◊ MARZLUFF	◊ SNETSINGER
◊ GORDON	◊ MICHELL	◊ STERRY
◊ GRANT	◊ OBMASCIK	◊ STOKES
◊ HELM	◊ O'BRIEN	◊ SVENSSON
◊ HUME	◊ PEPPERBERG	◊ THOMPSON
◊ KAUFMAN	◊ PETERSON	◊ WHITE

People with Birds Named for Them

```
N  I  S  S  A  C  E  I  S  V  F  X  V  G  S
E  B  X  D  E  R  T  N  O  P  U  D  A  S  A
S  O  X  L  S  K  G  E  I  A  E  G  O  P  R
W  N  N  U  O  P  R  Q  V  B  P  R  W  R  E
W  A  Y  O  T  B  S  P  O  H  A  B  F  L  K
I  P  F  G  S  I  U  I  T  R  O  S  E  U  Q
L  A  P  V  W  G  I  E  Q  T  T  W  N  Z  L
S  R  W  E  A  B  Q  S  T  E  O  E  O  I  E
O  T  L  M  I  J  U  E  L  R  Z  P  T  N  A
N  E  B  B  N  N  R  L  R  K  Y  S  T  O  C
B  E  C  C  S  I  E  A  L  E  C  O  U  C  H
L  G  L  F  O  R  B  L  Q  E  W  I  H  V  J
P  G  A  M  N  D  T  Y  S  D  R  E  W  T  R
C  E  R  D  F  R  N  S  P  O  K  H  R  E  B
M  D  K  P  L  E  U  G  A  T  N  O  M  B  B
```

◊ BARROW
◊ BEWICK
◊ BONAPARTE
◊ BOTTERI
◊ BREWER
◊ BULLER
◊ CASSIN
◊ CLARK

◊ COUCH
◊ DUPONT
◊ GAMBEL
◊ GOULD
◊ HUTTON
◊ LEACH
◊ LEWIS
◊ MONTAGU

◊ NELSON
◊ ROSS
◊ SABINE
◊ STELLER
◊ SWAINSON
◊ VAUX
◊ WILSON
◊ ZINO

Birds in the Harry Potter Universe

R E P O O W F X N I W D O R B
E Y T H E R M E S N J L E I U
K R P R E X R R Y E W T F A R
G I R R U D L K E A S V I L N
O H N O A V W R C A P A R B I
S I C G L H U I G F S U E A N
H A N S F T R Y G A W G B T G
A O L M I L Z F W A U I R D
W O R U D L S L U K L R R O A
K H V F A B A H Y E L E D S Y
V O V N N M R M E S O Y X S S
A O S J I P C S Z R W R I N D
G H T N J O B B E R K N O L L
E L G A E N E D L O G W J F P
N O E G D I W G I P Y K C L S

◊ ALBATROSS

◊ AUGUREY

◊ BRODWIN

◊ BURNING DAY

◊ DIRICAWL

◊ ERROL

◊ FAWKES

◊ FIREBIRD

◊ FLAMINGO

◊ FWOOPER

◊ GOLDEN EAGLE

◊ GOSHAWK

◊ HANS

◊ HARPY

◊ HEDWIG

◊ HERMES

◊ HOO-HOO

◊ JOBBER-KNOLL

◊ KINGFISHER

◊ PIGWIDGEON

◊ SNALLY-GASTER

◊ SNOWY

◊ SWALLOW

◊ VULTURE

Bird Families (Common Names)

```
N O C L A F A N Q F M J Z J T
X A Z V B M I T U R A C O R N
X L D U E G R E B E Z W O A A
S X C I H S T B C Q S P W E F
W N R T F I U A I V I S Y L Z
W E J S S S R K H C U G A K U
S A C E T A H C B C B M R Z H
R M M A C O I I C C I O U B V
E E R A A R R V Q N H M R F W
V D R T T D Y K G S T C F V C
O A Z S F R L O K T R L N U L
D I O E T O H I I H O A C I R
N O E G I P W E W R G K Y F F
H L O O N I Q H A N O S D G R
N I U G N E P I X O N U X E X
```

◊ BUSTARD   ◊ HOATZIN   ◊ PIGEON

◊ CARACARA   ◊ KAGU   ◊ RHEA

◊ CUCKOO   ◊ KIWI   ◊ SERIEMA

◊ DOVE   ◊ LOON   ◊ STORK

◊ FALCON   ◊ MESITE   ◊ SWAN

◊ FINCH   ◊ NIGHTJAR   ◊ TROGON

◊ FLAMINGO   ◊ OSTRICH   ◊ TROPICBIRD

◊ GREBE   ◊ PENGUIN   ◊ TURACO

Bird Profile: Great Hornbill

```
S R E M R A F V T E I D D E J
G E L S O C I A L D V I A C E
N Z U A S E I R E S S S R A S
I S L Q T I U R F T I P D F U
P F G N S I A M I A E E H I O
P E A I J A V N N N C R O G R
O M W D F G C G G I H S R H O
R A O P U T R A D C R A N T V
D L L F I E G U A O A L B S I
F E L V A I O M N S E L I E G
A T E T N U O I U T K Y L G U
M R Y G S T M A T E S C L R R
I C H E S T S E R O F P O A F
L E R U T C U R T S K C A L B
Y N I C K N A M E D K C E N F
```

Latin Name: *Buceros bicornis*

Family: *Bucerotidae*

Description: One of the largest members of the hornbill family, the great hornbill is distinctive for its large yellow beak and casque—a helmet-like structure above the bill. It has black wings, face, and chest, with a contrasting white neck, tail, and stomach and differences between the male and female are minor.

These social birds live in small family groups or flocks and normally mate for life. Males are seen engaging in casque-butting fights during courtship. They mostly eat a frugivorous—fruit-based—diet, particularly of figs.

Sounds: Great hornbills normally call in a loud series of grunts.

Distribution and habitat: They are found in deciduous and evergreen forests in a number of Asian countries including Nepal, Malaysia, and Vietnam.

Fun Fact: Hornbills are often nicknamed "farmers of the forest" due to the vital role their droppings play in the dispersal of fruit seeds.

```
D E I K E V O D A H D Y G E D
E A D A O N O N A I R U A D D
D I A M O N D D O V E D L L A
Z C D R A B C A A I A D C I R
O I O F D E U P R M W U T H T
D H K W E U C E A K Y N R M F
O P A O G N O R D K E E E K O
D R H S D O A E S K T Y S T R
F O D I K X T U I R F Z E Z D
D M I R D T D R A C D A D D Y
A I P I O O E D N I L N U D Q
E D P D C D G U A R N D U C K
V G E W E F X E D U N N O C K
A K R I K K C A D T C B A E E
D O D L O T I D A R O D G I D
```

◊ DAMARA
  TERN

◊ DARK-EYED
  JUNCO

◊ DARTER

◊ DARTFORD
  WARBLER

◊ DAURIAN
  JACKDAW

◊ DEGODI LARK

◊ DESERT
  FINCH

◊ DIAMOND
  DOVE

◊ DIEDERIK
  CUCKOO

◊ DIMORPHIC
  FANTAIL

◊ DIPPER

◊ DODO

◊ DORADITO

◊ DOTTED
  TANAGER

◊ DOVEKIE

◊ DRAB
  SEEDEATER

◊ DRONGO
  CUCKOO

◊ DUCK

◊ DULIT
  FROGMOUTH

◊ DUNE LARK

◊ DUNLIN

◊ DUNNOCK

◊ DUSKY TIT

◊ DWARF JAY

```
B B N U R T E G N I L S O G D
U M U Q E R E L A E U Q S O R
J E N N Y D K L I H G N N U E
R S G X D J C S L N U Q F D K
O Y U J W C I K S U E M V G A
C V T B E T H L X Q P V N R E
P T L G A K C Y O F U I U T U
P G U N K D A H H O L A E J Q
T N O I R I U J E T N E B K S
E I P L S Z X L S E K L T E Q
L L M G O P X E T L P G E R Q
W K E D E Q N Y K G W E D T C
O C M E N H E A J A R V R A C
V U P L Y J K S R E P P A L F
G D A F G N I L H C T A H K C
```

◊ CHEEPER   ◊ GOSLING   ◊ OWLET

◊ CHICK   ◊ HATCHLING   ◊ PEEP

◊ CYGNET   ◊ JAKE   ◊ POULT

◊ DUCKLING   ◊ JENNY   ◊ PULLET

◊ EAGLET   ◊ JUVENILE   ◊ SQUAB

◊ EYAS   ◊ KEET   ◊ SQUEAKER

◊ FLAPPER   ◊ LOONLET   ◊ SQUEALER

◊ FLEDGLING   ◊ NESTLING   ◊ SUBADULT

```
H C N I F F A H C L G N H E Q
U E T I K K C A L B T P V P G
G B L A C K B I R D U O P N D
V J X T F F B V M J D K I L Y
L R S S U N L A D K I L F W Z
M E P I R A G W C N R N L O Z
H H T O S P D O G A N I L L R
P C H T I K R F T V L B N L M
A T S E U C I S H S C O W A U
R A P R F S B N L S E R R W U
A C A N H L N G M G U T O S Z
K Y R E X R U Z I B I R W W M
E L R A K L S P M N D I H U Q
E F O O L T J A K V F X Q T V
T E W C O A L T I T E U L B G
```

◊ BLACK KITE	◊ HORNBILL	◊ SISKIN
◊ BLACKBIRD	◊ KINGFISHER	◊ SPARROW
◊ BLUE TIT	◊ MAGPIE	◊ STARLING
◊ CHAFFINCH	◊ MARTIN	◊ SUNBIRD
◊ COAL TIT	◊ PARAKEET	◊ SWALLOW
◊ CROW	◊ PIGEON	◊ SWIFT
◊ FLYCATCHER	◊ ROBIN	◊ TERN
◊ GULL	◊ ROCK DOVE	◊ THRUSH

```
S W O R R A P S P S D H G C V
F A T H E R K P W R Y R G N A
I O P I X R R U I H V S O W P
T H V P O E U B B U E Y O R T
H L I T T L E Y L J B R E C N
E P S T K U E T W I C K E H N
M U Y K L B U E R E W N L I A
I O L B Y R S D H A S Z G C W
G S E E E Y T H E Y R A K S
H H X S S A T Y L T K F E E K
T H E W I L D G E E S E N N C
Y B A T M A N O D E K R O M A
B T X P L A D R A W O H R G L
X O B D R I B C X S V C I R B
T H E E S E T L A M E H T A G
```

◊ *ANGRY BIRDS*

◊ *BATMAN AND ROBIN*

◊ *BIRD BOX*

◊ *BIRDY*

◊ *BLACK SWAN*

◊ *BYE BYE BIRDIE*

◊ *CHICKEN LITTLE*

◊ *DUCK SOUP*

◊ *FATHER GOOSE*

◊ *GAME FOR VULTURES*

◊ *HOWARD THE DUCK*

◊ *IRON EAGLE*

◊ *LADYHAWKE*

◊ *LITTLE BIRDS*

◊ *PRETTY BIRD*

◊ *SPARROWS CAN'T SING*

◊ *STORKS*

◊ *SWEET BIRD OF YOUTH*

◊ *THE BLUE BIRD*

◊ *THE CROW*

◊ *THE MALTESE FALCON*

◊ *THE MIGHTY DUCKS*

◊ *THE WILD GEESE*

◊ *WHERE EAGLES DARE*

Bird Derived First Names

```
V B N C W E A X Y U Y A C W R
Y I R X E A N L I N I A W A G
O R B C A O O I E N C K V J M
C D R H U N W F D M E R I U Y
E I A J V E C K D N O O L L C
C E N L Q H O R S P A L H A Q
A U U C P C Z A Y E A L I P U
T R O N S P E L A C P L E H H
T L V A A L X A I E H H O C P
M E V I R M R H V G H A O M D
N O X E D D N A D L Q R L R A
W E M E R L I N M E D M Q N A
T X V X P J B O W O R M P O L
M E G A A M O J V O S Y Z M G
Z O P Y R Q R E P Q J N N K E
```

◊ ARVID

◊ BIRDIE

◊ BRAN

◊ CALLUM

◊ CELANDINE

◊ CHENOA

◊ CIRCE

◊ COLM

◊ DERYN

◊ DOVE

◊ GAWAIN

◊ JAY

◊ JONAH

◊ LARK

◊ MANU

◊ MERLE

◊ MERLIN

◊ PALOMA

◊ PHILOMELA

◊ PHOENIX

◊ RAVEN

◊ RHEA

◊ ROBIN

◊ SEPHORA

Bird Profile: Common Swift

```
T I C L L I R H S D N U O S S
S R D G I N T N A S A E L P G
E E E E F S N O I T A C O L N
T T V C E E T S E V A E H E I
S H E O T I A F R I C A G Y W
A G I L I D O H I T H G I L F
F I L O M O E E I W U I H E Y
Y L E N E B E U P O S C N D R
D E B I R C S E D E O R Y I E
E V F E S R E V U M O H H W V
K E A S U L S R M B N W O L F
R L C P S P A O R R E T A W E
O S T C E S N I N O I T O M M
F G O N I B A S O C I A L N A
N P T A L A U D I V I D N I N
```

Latin Name: *Apus apus*

Family: *Apodidae*

Description: The common swift, like other swifts, is most often seen in motion. They have forked tails and pulled-back wings which create a crescent-shape when in flight. They are blackish-brown with lighter feathers below the chin. They nest up high, in eaves and other similar locations, in large colonies and are highly social birds.

Sounds: The sounds of the swift are usually described as shrill and are certainly not the most pleasant birdsong!

Distribution and Habitat: Widely distributed across Eurasia and Africa, they are often seen in pursuit of insects above bodies of water.

Fun Facts: As their name suggests, these birds are very fast, in fact they are the fastest of all birds in level flight. So much of their time is spent in flight that they even sleep while airborne, and one long-lived individual was believed to have flown more than four million miles in its lifetime!

```
N U M H T N A R O M R O C P H
N A D D T H F O J U E M I G K
M A C I R O A M B R E D R S E
E X M S F V H N C L I U Z I E
S T P O U O O T E Z M P P B R
O S A G R R P K A I I M V I G
P Y N N S Y T Y S Z U K B O U
O R A E G A C E X L C J L E A
T P Y E U A C E L O B L R S M
A O A S C F T U C O M U H J H
M U R V K D H A I W T E N S U
I A J D A C E R M L R T I S G
A K A N O P K I U A J A N Y I
J A V K W V R V H J N T U K N
R I S A D J E Y R K P U M Z A
```

◊ ASHERAH

◊ CHULLUMPI

◊ CORMORANT

◊ DOVE

◊ EGYPT

◊ ETRUSCAN

◊ GREEK

◊ HUGIN

◊ IBIS

◊ MAORI

◊ MELEK TAUS

◊ MESO-
POTAMIA

◊ MUNIN

◊ NORSE

◊ OWL

◊ PEACOCK

◊ POUAKAI

◊ ROMAN

◊ SIMURGH

◊ TANGATA
MANU

◊ THOTH

◊ VAJRAYANA

◊ VULTURE

◊ YAZIDI

```
H F O N E W Z E A L A N D J M
R I O E V Y U M M G N A S K L
O O T Q L X R H I H L I E Q U
R R N S Z T U I A R S B R H R
E D E C O M T L A L P I A P O
P L G X B G O I A F O M N A C
M A I O H G A N L E A A S R K
E N L H N Q D P A B C N Y T H
K D N A C I R F A H T U O S O
T M A C A R O N I L Y Q B N P
M A G E L L A N I C A L T I P
U L Q E F E I L E D A G P H E
L N B G N I K T A Y X I E C R
N O R T H E R N O Y E U G W F
Q J D E T S E R C T C E R E F
```

◊ ADELIE

◊ AFRICAN

◊ ANGOLA

◊ CHILE

◊ CHINSTRAP

◊ EMPEROR

◊ ERECT-
CRESTED

◊ FAIRY

◊ FIORDLAND

◊ GALAPAGOS

◊ GENTOO

◊ HUMBOLDT

◊ ISLAND

◊ KING

◊ LITTLE

◊ MACARONI

◊ MAGELLANIC

◊ NAMIBIA

◊ NEW
ZEALAND

◊ NORTHERN

◊ ROCKHOPPER

◊ ROYAL

◊ SNARES

◊ SOUTH
AFRICA

Birdwatching Hotspots

```
L C A P E M A Y M E M O O R B
A U T J A I B M A G W O D T O
N H A V S E L O U I S I A N A
A D R B H U T A N K V R W E T
T N I R A N O R J A A K N A R
N A R L L T A T C B K K A I O
A L A L A G M I O R A W I S D
P A V G S T A C V E H E T U A
Y G O V K M I L A G B B U L U
P A P U A N E W G U I N E A C
Q N A J O D I X N R P I L D E
M M E D S P D A B K G B A N A
P A N J F R D J A N D A M A N
L I N S E D A L G R E V E S Y
M V Q U Y E L L A V T F I R X
```

◊ ALASKA

◊ ALEUTIAN

◊ ANDALUSIA

◊ ANDAMAN

◊ BHUTAN

◊ BROOME

◊ CAPE MAY

◊ DANUBE

◊ ECUADOR

◊ EVERGLADES

◊ GAMBIA

◊ JAMAICA

◊ KAKUM

◊ KRUGER

◊ LOUISIANA

◊ MANU

◊ MINDO

◊ NAGALAND

◊ NICOBAR

◊ OTAGO

◊ PANTANAL

◊ PAPUA NEW
 GUINEA

◊ RIFT VALLEY

◊ VARIRATA

```
T E R E K S A N D P I P E R I
U P X C H I M N E Y S W I F T
N I L R E L B R A W E G D E S
J O I I S I B I Y S S O L G X
R K R L A U G H I N G D O V E
E A S E K R O T S K C A L B G
X J K F H T R K G S R N U M O
F B F U R E V E O M W S T U L
F M Y W H O L V T O T N A T D
K K E P K C C P R A R L H E C
X M V H U K V K R I W I C S R
S I F L N F X D D U U W N W E
R V A R O S F B B O P P I A S
S A N D E R L I N G V U H N T
T E R G E Y W O N S R E W Q Y
```

◊ BLACK STORK

◊ BUSTARD

◊ CHIMNEY
SWIFT

◊ CHUKAR

◊ GLOSSY IBIS

◊ GOLDCREST

◊ LAUGHING
DOVE

◊ MUTE SWAN

◊ PUFFIN

◊ PURPLE
HERON

◊ ROCK DOVE

◊ ROOK

◊ SANDERLING

◊ SEDGE
WARBLER

◊ SHRIKE

◊ SMEW

◊ SNOWY
EGRET

◊ SORA

◊ TEREK
SANDPIPER

◊ WATER RAIL

◊ WHINCHAT

```
T  L  E  T  K  L  S  E  A  D  A  L  N  E  I
Y  S  B  K  E  Z  E  V  A  X  E  N  X  L  A
X  D  A  Q  A  N  A  S  T  A  W  N  U  T  E
E  O  T  E  O  L  N  E  E  E  N  Z  I  R  L
I  A  N  A  L  L  J  I  L  P  A  H  E  L  E
L  U  L  G  U  L  G  T  L  L  C  N  E  V  Q
A  T  U  C  I  K  T  N  E  N  N  A  O  U  L
L  I  Y  D  R  I  R  L  I  U  F  L  L  R  O
E  S  T  A  L  A  E  F  R  W  F  Y  N  O  V
S  H  L  P  G  G  T  G  A  A  P  I  E  D  E
S  W  R  G  R  S  O  R  E  A  K  A  I  A  B
E  L  A  A  U  L  B  L  E  P  A  Z  L  R  I
R  L  L  C  G  L  L  V  M  P  J  A  W  B  R
E  F  O  I  E  E  R  I  L  Y  E  R  L  A  D
L  L  H  R  L  O  L  E  N  E  D  L  D  L  A
```

◊ LABRADOR DUCK

◊ LAGGAR FALCON

◊ LAKE DUCK

◊ LANAI HOOKBILL

◊ LAPWING

◊ LARGE NILTAVA

◊ LARK

◊ LAVA GULL

◊ LAZULI BUNTING

◊ LEAF-LOVE

◊ LEAF-WARBLER

◊ LEAST TERN

◊ LEPE CISTICOLA

◊ LESSER RHEA

◊ LIDTH'S JAY

◊ LIMPKIN

◊ LINED SEEDEATER

◊ LINNET

◊ LITTLE STINT

◊ LOCUSTFINCH

◊ LOETOE MONARCH

◊ LOGRUNNER

◊ LOVEBIRD

◊ LUCY'S WARBLER

Bird Profile:
Magnificent Bird-of-Paradise

```
E F G I B L A C K R A D G S N
B S N D R E N I A L P A N M E
T A I O P I N N T P R Z I R D
G L N O I A D A N T E O N O L
C N N D U H P E M N A I N F O
U S I C S Q S U S E D N U R G
R E W L F T R A A C Y D T E E
V I R V P O A U F I E O S P T
E C A R E A U G T F X N P S A
D E T E Y N S N E I G E T E R
A P S E L A M X D N B S K M O
N S C O U R T I N G R I N U B
C A F O R E S T S A O A O L A
E L I A T R E V O M W C W P L
Y E L L O W C L E A N I N G E
```

Latin Name: *Cicinnurus magnificus*

Family: *Paradisaeidae*

Description: The male magnificent bird-of-paradise truly lives up to its name, with golden wings, a paler yellow cape, an iridescent turquoise breast, and long, curved, blue tail plumes. It also has brown, dark red, and black feathers. The female is a plainer bird with lighter brown feathers and whiteish bands.

The males of all species of birds-of-paradise are known for their elaborate plumage and extravagant courting dances with those exhibiting the most stunning performances and feathers winning females over.

Distribution and habitat: They can be found in the forests of Papua New Guinea and Indonesia.

Fun Fact: Before a male performs his courtship dance, displaying his cape in a halo-like fashion while hanging from a sapling, he makes sure everything is ready, clearing and cleaning both himself and the area to set the "stage".

```
E W E V P A B U S E E S E S D
C E C U R T B B C X C S N M Q
U D U E M E I U C C U P O C B
D Z D N C M D U H F R M O A A
O F E U O S S A F O P Z S B D
R T R U N E R E F K S R E O D
P B S A A T J U I C E O M O U
R S R A R S S N Y P J O K S C
E T L E I E H R R E O M Z E E
V H U I I L E O I S A U E G O
O S G Q O C D I E S H R C O Y
E K W O L U Z W E S O R U S O
W Q S U C G T E A P A O D E S
D E S E L K E S U T B O E S E
F E S O O K E S U S I M S E C
```

◊ ABUSE

◊ ADDUCE

◊ BRUCE

◊ CABOOSE

◊ CHARTREUSE

◊ EFFUSE

◊ EXCUSE

◊ JUICE

◊ LOOSE

◊ MISUSE

◊ MOOSE

◊ MOUSSE

◊ NOOSE

◊ OBTUSE

◊ OVER-
   PRODUCE

◊ PROFUSE

◊ RECLUSE

◊ REDUCE

◊ REPRODUCE

◊ SEDUCE

◊ SPRUCE

◊ TRANSDUCE

◊ TRUCE

◊ ZEUS

My Doves
by Elizabeth Barrett Browning

```
S R E H T A E F T N E T N O C
D H Y M O T I O N Y E R G L G
N G L T I U R F T U N E N A N
U A E O P W A R M T H Z I P I
O N T W O L D F L O W E R S H
S N A U L K O Q N D A E E E T
B R L I R W V F A O V R T Z I
D I N D D E E A E W E B T H W
T G S M W N S N C N O S I R P
R N E R L K I T O S U N L I T
P B E S A I C A D E L I G H T
A G R P R T T S R A R N E A T
C I T O L I S T E N L T S I M
E U L B W O A I L T H G I R Z
S U D D E N J C F E R E T A W
```

My little doves have left a
  nest
Upon an Indian tree,
Whose leaves fantastic take
  their rest
Or motion from the sea;
For, ever there the sea-winds
  go
With sunlit paces to and fro.

The tropic flowers looked up
  to it,
The tropic stars looked down,
And there my little doves did
  sit
With feathers softly brown,
And glittering eyes that
  showed their right
To general Nature's deep
  delight.

My little doves were ta'en
  away
From that glad nest of theirs,
Across an ocean rolling grey,
And tempest-clouded airs.
My little doves who lately
  knew
The sky and wave by warmth
  and blue.

And now, within the city
  prison
In mist and chillness pent,
With sudden upward look
  they listen
For sounds of past content,
For lapse of water, smell of
  breeze,
Or nut-fruit falling from the
  trees.

Game Birds

```
L W O F R U P S T P K N M L W
G N Z L W O F A E P C A A I O
I Y E K R U T A S R O N V A C
N Q N L A W C T U A C A L U T
U E N R M O A I O I W P W Q I
P K G A C T I I R R O O O J Y
Y U N K C N A U G I N G F E L
S W O S S A R U C E S A A D W
O Y J Y I X L D C C O R E O O
T E W T N A S A E H P T N P F
M L L Y B O B W H I T E I A B
T K C A B E R I F C B X U G U
P T A R M I G A N K A W G E R
N I L O C N A R F E O H I M C
P A R T R I D G E N R Y C G S
```

◊ ARGUS

◊ BOBWHITE

◊ CHACHALACA

◊ CURASSOW

◊ FIREBACK

◊ FRANCOLIN

◊ GROUSE

◊ GUAN

◊ GUINEAFOWL

◊ MALEO

◊ MEGAPODE

◊ PARTRIDGE

◊ PEACOCK

◊ PEAFOWL

◊ PHEASANT

◊ PRAIRIE
   CHICKEN

◊ PTARMIGAN

◊ QUAIL

◊ SCRUBFOWL

◊ SNOWCOCK

◊ SPURFOWL

◊ TRAGOPAN

◊ TURKEY

◊ WAIGEO

```
A T F I W S E N I P L A H F A
A J A L A A P O M Y N A U K A
K C U D N A E D N A A Y I A S
A O A A T I U S W I F T L E T
F F A B B A U A I N A I N A R
R E L T I R A B U S U O G E A
I N O A R G Z A H Y C R A H P
C A P T D U A Y V L A C A O I
A P A L I S B K A O C A N K A
N A I A E U A F I E C E U E G
P P K V L E R N N K R E N H N
I A A B Q U K T H W I S T O I
T I U A M A O E T A G K V K H
T L W A T R P N K D I O I A N
A X A K A L A T X A O A A G A
```

◊ ACCENTOR

◊ AFRICAN PITTA

◊ AKALAT

◊ 'AKEKE'E

◊ 'AKIAPOLA'AU

◊ 'AKIKIKI

◊ 'AKOHEKOHE

◊ ALPINE SWIFT

◊ AMAUI

◊ AMUR FALCON

◊ ANDEAN DUCK

◊ ANHINGA

◊ 'ANIANIAU

◊ ANTBIRD

◊ ANTWREN

◊ APALIS

◊ 'APAPANE

◊ APO MYNA

◊ ARGUS

◊ ASHY BULBUL

◊ ASTRAPIA

◊ ATIU SWIFTLET

◊ AUK

◊ AVOCET

Birds of Africa

```
F A H O K L A M E U L B A R K
T F K O R I B U S T A R D E L
A E U I W H I M B R E L T V L
E G L R D U N L I N T Y F O I
B V L G P T O T E G E L I L B
Y V O H A M E R K O P I W P N
S J V D F E W C X Z A A S B R
H Y E L N V Y P F G C U E A O
O C B R U O E N V J N Q C R H
E H I L D C M U W B O E R C B
B Q R R K L L E I A N U A H D
I T D E T T U R L I T L C Z B
L J R F U S D Q J F T B S F G
L M A R A B O U S T O R K M G
V R E O G N I M A L F E E X H
```

◊ BLUE MALKOHA

◊ BLUE QUAIL

◊ CAPE TEAL

◊ CRAB-PLOVER

◊ DUNLIN

◊ FLAMINGO

◊ HAMERKOP

◊ HORNBILL

◊ KORI BUSTARD

◊ LEMON DOVE

◊ LOVEBIRD

◊ MARABOU STORK

◊ OSTRICH

◊ OXPECKER

◊ RUFF

◊ SCARCE SWIFT

◊ SHOEBILL

◊ SUNBIRD

◊ TAWNY EAGLE

◊ VULTURE

◊ WHIMBREL

Solutions

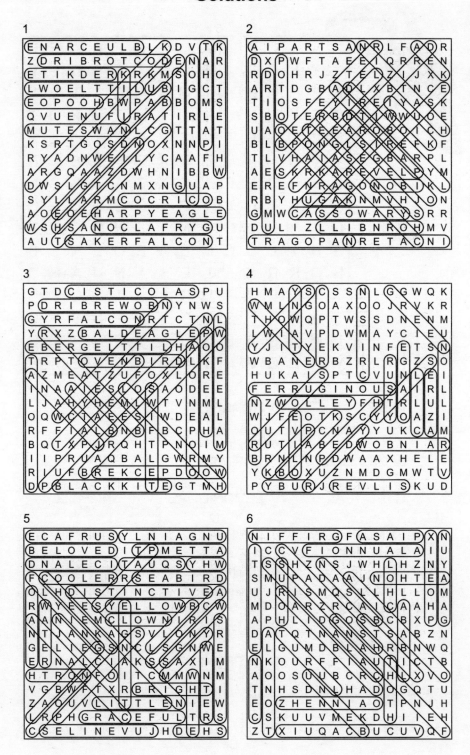

Solutions

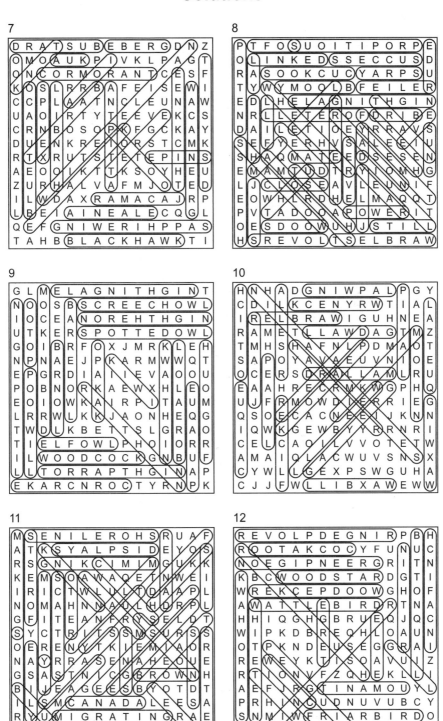

Solutions

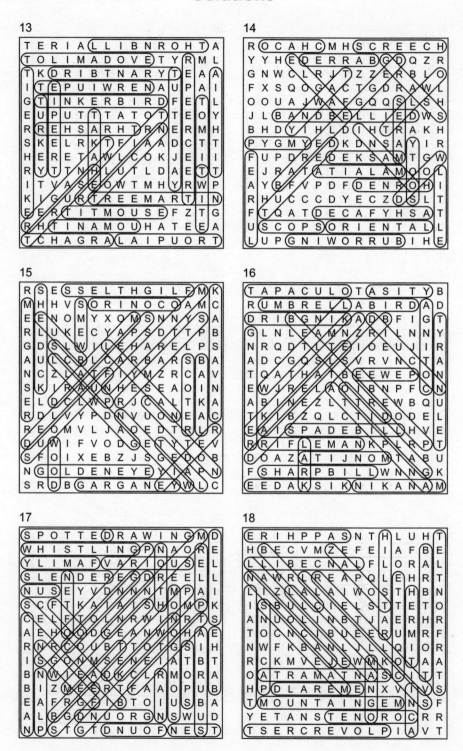

Solutions

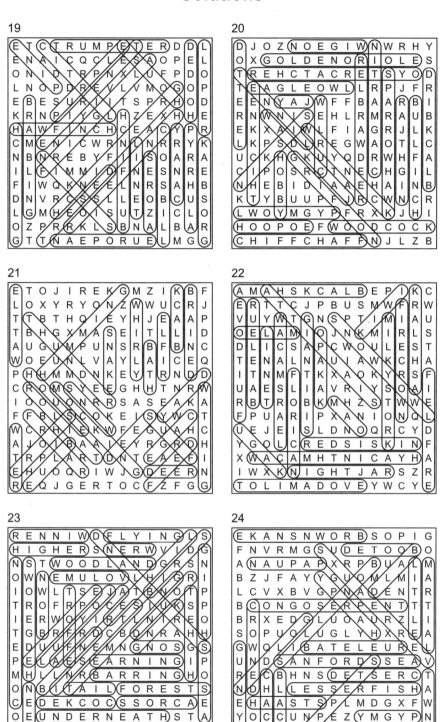

Solutions

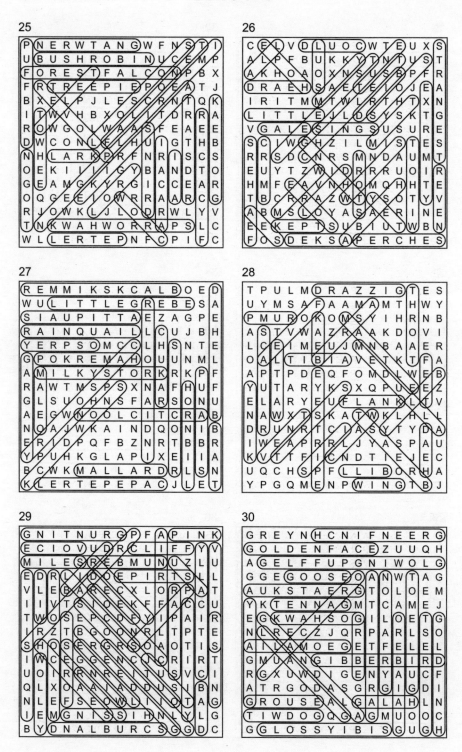

25

26

27

28

29

30

Solutions

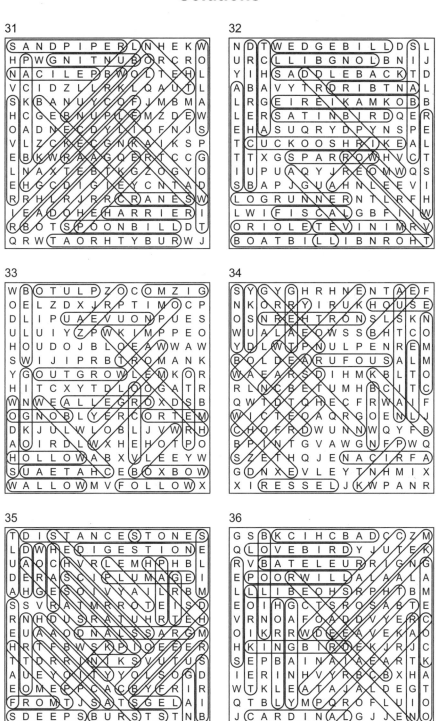

Solutions

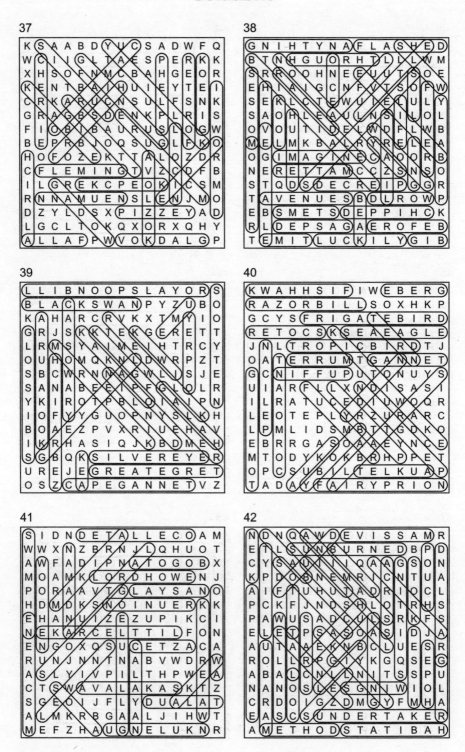

Solutions

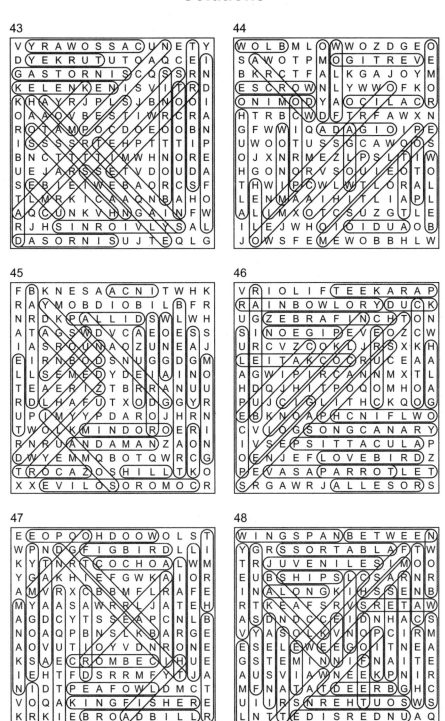

Solutions

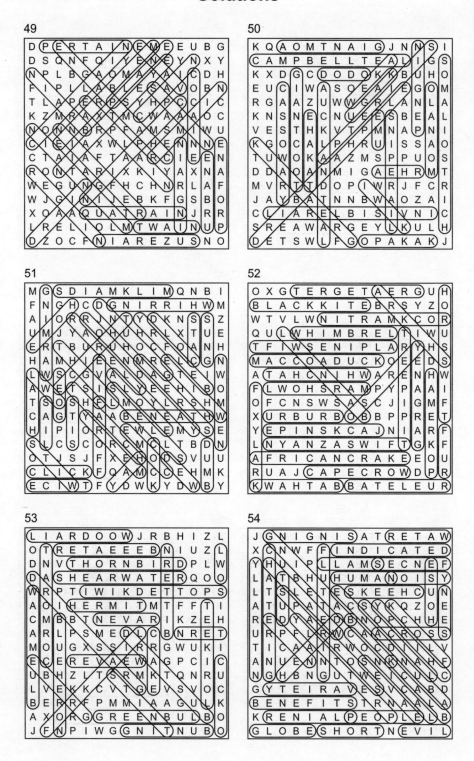

Solutions

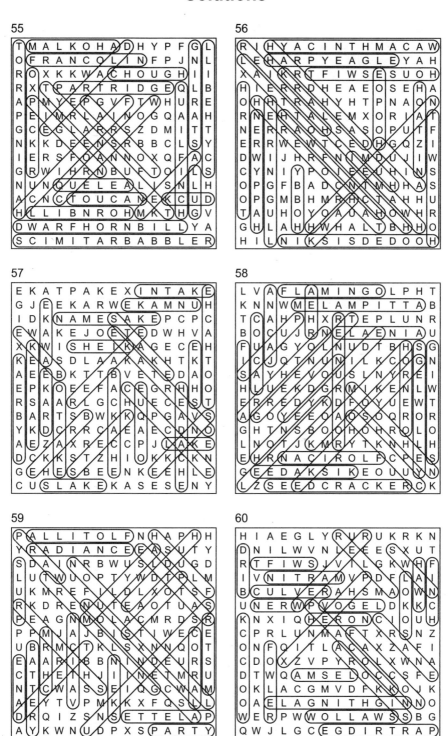

Solutions

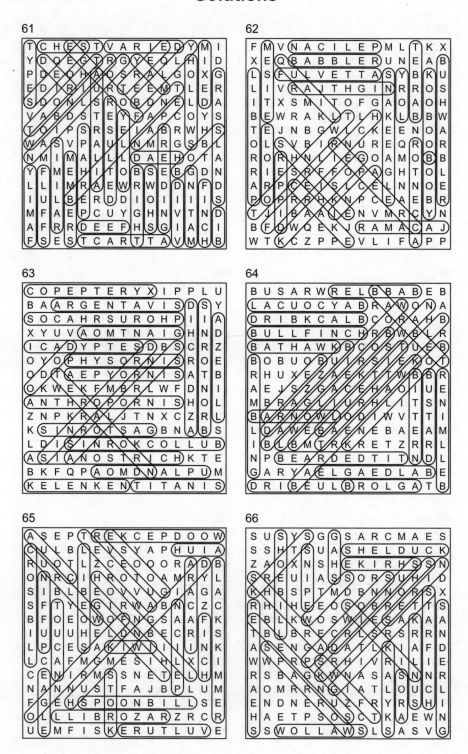

Solutions

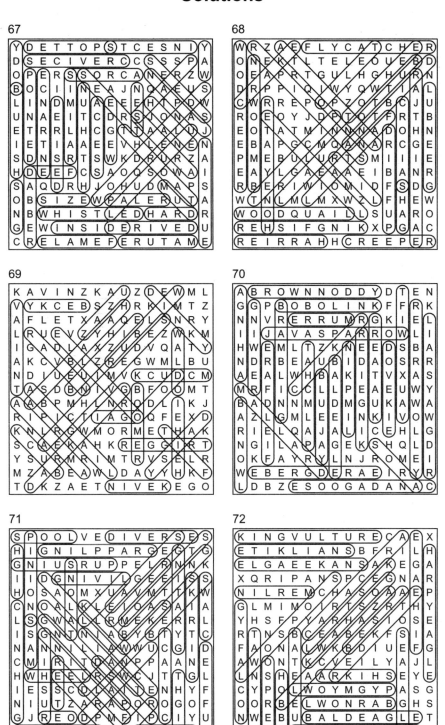

Solutions

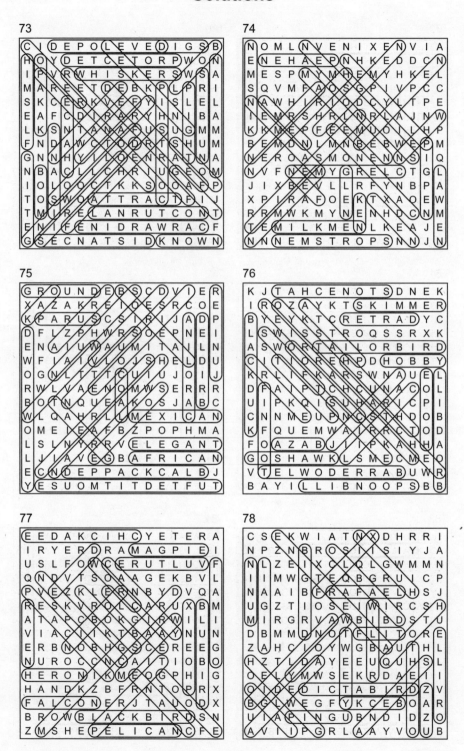

Solutions

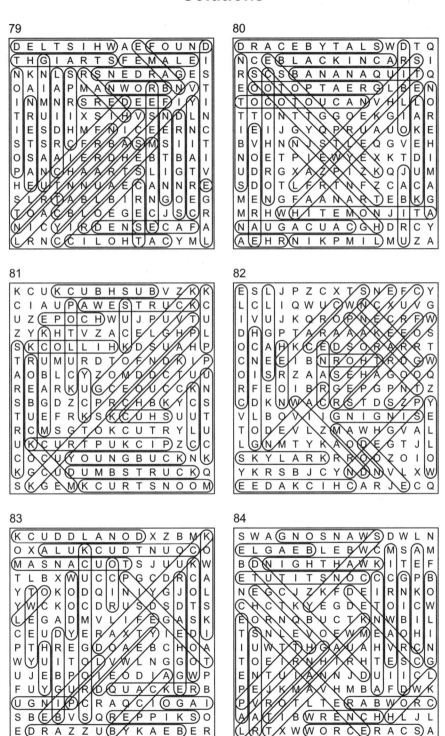

Solutions

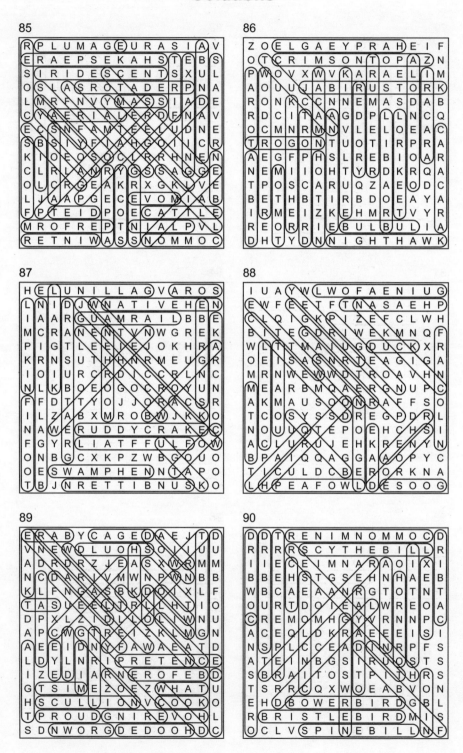

85

86

87

88

89

90

Solutions

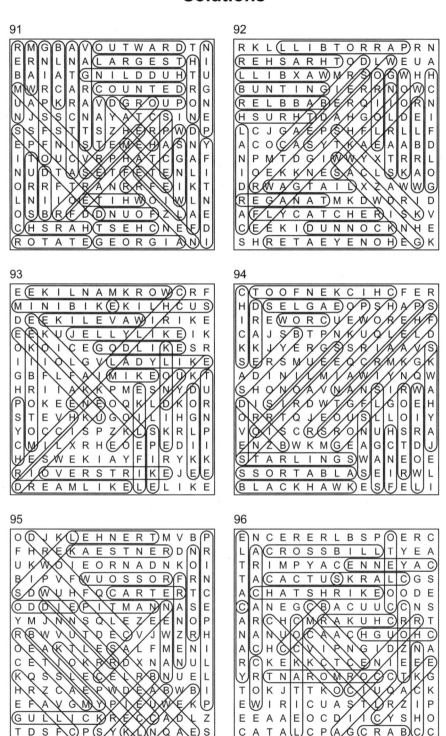

Solutions

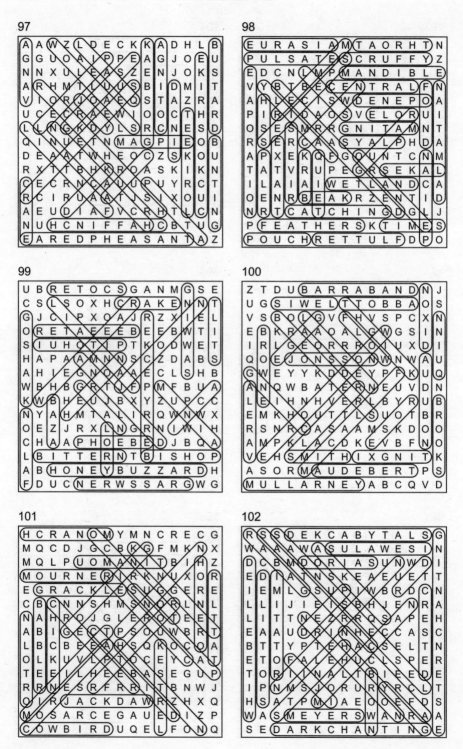

Solutions

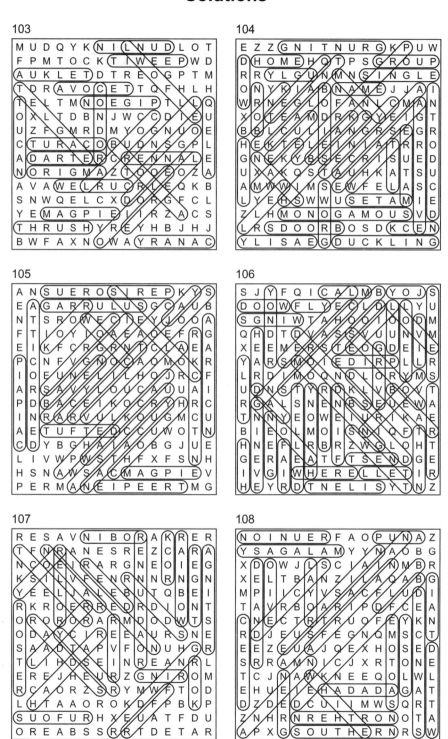

Solutions

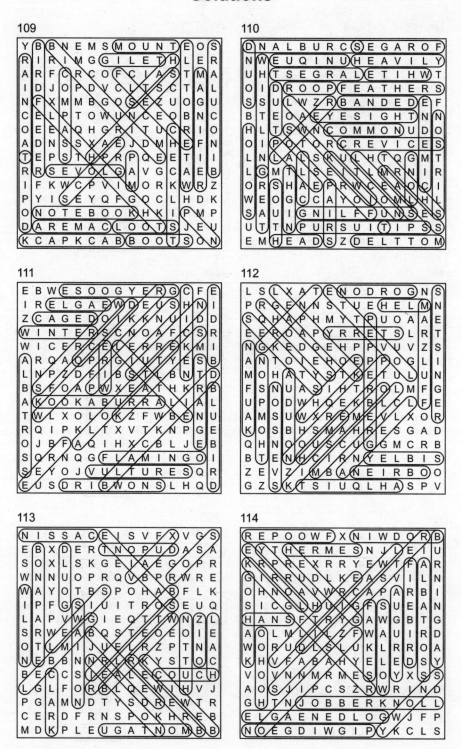

Solutions

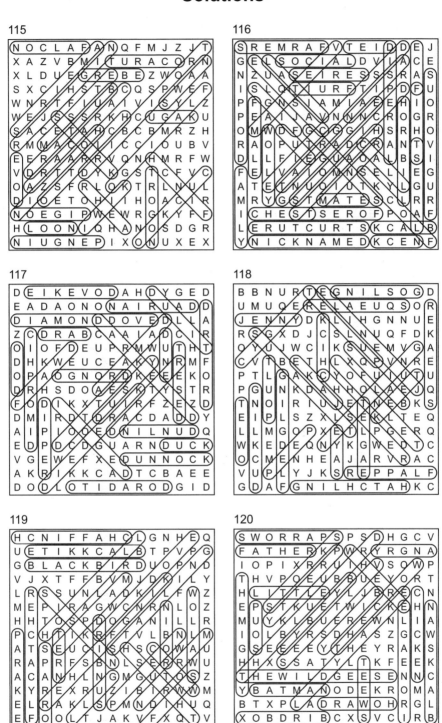

115

116

117

118

119

120

Solutions

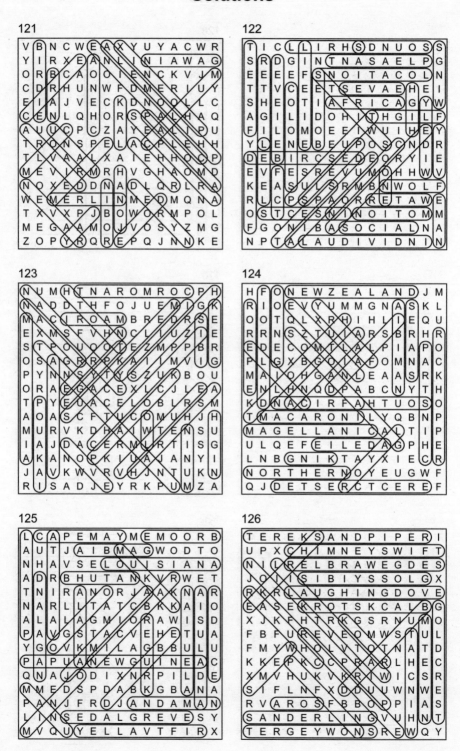

Solutions

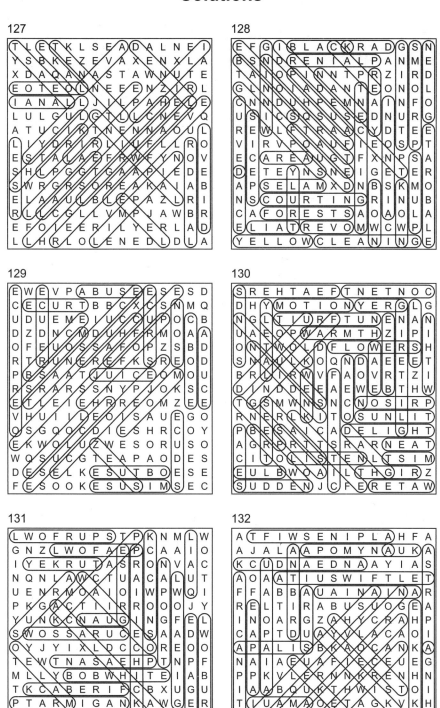

Solutions

133

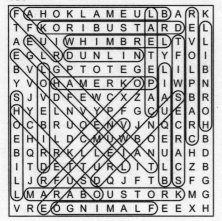